YES MINISTER

YES MINISTER

THE DIARIES OF A CABINET MINISTER
BY THE RT HON. JAMES HACKER MP

Volume Three

Edited by Jonathan Lynn
and Antony Jay

BRITISH BROADCASTING CORPORATION

Published by the
British Broadcasting Corporation
35 Marylebone High Street
London W1M 4AA

ISBN 0 563 20196 7
First published 1983

© Jonathan Lynn and Antony Jay 1983

Typeset by Phoenix Photosetting, Chatham
Printed in England
by Mackays of Chatham Ltd

Contents

Editors' Note

The third volume of the Hacker diaries presented the editors with a new problem: Volumes I and II had been transcribed in the great stateman's own lifetime, and he had read them through and made some preliminary suggestions of his own as to selection and arrangement. But Volume III in common with all the later volumes had yet to be transcribed from the cassette recordings when the bell rang for the Last Division.

As a result we were confronted by a much more formidable task: not only was there a far greater mass of unorganised material to assimilate, but it also seemed that Hacker's speech became more and more indistinct as each recording session progressed. This may have been due to a fault in the recording machine, but it did not make our task any easier.

As it was, the huge amount of material served to emphasise one of the principal problems of interpreting the writings of any politician. He processes events in a variety of ways, so that readers have to make their own judgement as to whether any given statement represents

    (a) what happened
    (b) what he believed happened
    (c) what he would like to have happened
    (d) what he wants others to believe happened
    (e) what he wants others to believe he believed happened

As a general rule, politicians' memories are less reliable about failures than successes, and about distant events than recent ones. Since Hacker's career, like all politicians', consisted mostly of failures, and since by Volume III he was becoming less punctilious about dictating his diary each evening, this volume might have had only small historical value. What saves it is the fact that because it was never transcribed, the great man was unable to make any alterations or excisions in the light of subsequent events. We believe that

7

this fact, added to the experience and insight gained from editing the two earlier volumes, has enabled us to select from the morass a document of unique value to students of the period.

As before we owe a great debt of gratitude to the Public Records Office and to the Trustees of the voluminous Appleby papers, which, as we have acknowledged in earlier volumes, we were privileged to be able to supplement from revelations in the few lucid moments of Sir Humphrey Appleby's last ravings. For this we would like to record our gratitude to the staff of St Dympna's Hospital for the Elderly Deranged. And of course we are continually grateful to Sir Bernard Woolley GCB, former Head of the Civil Service and Hacker's Private Secretary for the period covered by the diaries, who has once again given generously of his time and checked our selection against his own memory and records. Nevertheless any responsibility for errors and omissions is, of course, entirely our own.

Jonathan Lynn
Antony Jay
Hacker College, Oxford.
September, 2019 AD

1
Equal Opportunities

June 7th

Today was a fairly quiet Saturday afternoon in the constituency. The end of our first complete Parliamentary session is approaching and I was feeling that I've done pretty well, one way or another: no great cock-ups after my first ever year in office (or at least, none which we haven't survived somehow)[1] and I have a sense that I am beginning to understand the administrative machine at last.

You may think that a year is rather too long a period in which to achieve an understanding of the one department of which I am the titular head. In political terms, of course, that's true. Nonetheless if, had I become Chairman of ICI after a lifetime as a journalist and polytechnic lecturer and with no previous experience of running a major industry, I had a thorough understanding of how it all worked after only one year, I would be considered a great success.

We politicians blunder into Whitehall like babes in the wood. So few of us have ever run *anything* before, other than a medical practice, a law firm, or a political journal – and suddenly we find ourselves the head of a ministry with between twenty thousand and a hundred thousand employees.

All in all, I think we do pretty well! [*It was in this bullish mood that Hacker had agreed that day to give an interview to Cathy Webb, a fourth former in one of the comprehensive schools in Hacker's constituency*].[2]

However my enthusiastic feelings about my first year in office were, I must admit, a little shaken after I was interviewed at teatime by a precocious schoolgirl for the school magazine.

She began by asking me how I had reached my present eminent position. I summarised my political career so far, culminating, I

[1] See *Yes Minister* Volumes One and Two.
[2] Birmingham South-East.

said, with carefully calculated modesty, 'with the moment when the Prime Minister saw fit, for whatever reason, to invite one to join the Cabinet and, well, here one is.' I didn't want to seem conceited. In my experience the young have a nose for that sort of thing.

She asked me if it isn't a terrific responsibility. I explained to her that if one chooses, as I have chosen, to dedicate one's life to public service, the service of others, then responsibility is one of those things one has to accept.

Cathy was full of admiration, I could see it in her eyes. 'But all that power . . .' she murmured.

'I know, I know,' I replied, attempting the casual air of a man who is used to it. 'Frightening, in a way. But actually, Cathy . . .' (I was careful to use her name, of course, because it showed I did not consider myself above my constituents, even schoolchildren – future voters, after all). '. . . this power actually makes one rather humble!'

Annie[1] hurried in and interrupted me. The phone had been ringing elsewhere in the house.

'Bernard just rang, oh Humble One,' she said. I *wish* she wouldn't send me up like that in front of other people. I mean, I've got a pretty good sense of humour, but there is a limit.

She went on to tell me that Central House[2] wanted me to see some programme on television. On BBC2.

I had already remembered the wretched programme, and made a note *not* to watch.

'Oh Lord,' I said. 'Maureen Watkins MP. One of our backbenchers – not my favourite lady, a rampaging feminist, I don't think I'll bother.'

In the nick of time I noticed Cathy making a note. I had to explain that my remark was 'off the record', a concept that she seemed to have some difficulty with. It reminded me how lucky we are to have those well-trained lobby correspondents to deal with most of the time.

Anyway, she crossed it out. But to my surprise she spoke up in defence of Maureen Watkins.

'I like her,' she said. 'Don't you think that women are still exploited? All of my friends in 4B think that they are exploited at work and at home and that it's still a world designed by men and run by men for the convenience of men.'

[1] Mrs Hacker.
[2] Hacker's Party HQ.

10

I was slightly surprised by this little speech. It didn't sound entirely . . . home-grown, if you know what I mean. Cathy must have realised, because she had the grace to add: 'You know – like she says.'

I must say, I'm getting a bit fed up with all this feminist crap. Nowadays, if you so much as compliment a woman on her appearance, you're told you're a sexist. This dreadful lesbian lobby is getting everywhere.

So I decided to argue the point with young Cathy. 'Surely it's not like that any longer,' I said with a warm smile. 'Anyway, she doesn't carry any weight in the House, thank goodness.'

'Not in the House, perhaps,' interjected Annie. 'It's full of men.'

I thanked my dear wife for her helpful comment, renewed my smile in Cathy's direction, and asked her if there was anything else she wanted to know.

'Just one last question,' she said. 'As a Cabinet Minister with all this power, what have you actually achieved?'

I was pleased to answer that question. It seemed an easy one. 'Achieved?' I repeated reflectively. 'Well, all sorts of things. Membership of the Privy Council, membership of the party policy committee . . .'

She interrupted. It seemed that she wanted to make the question more specific. What, she wanted to know, had I actually done that makes life better for other people.

Well, of course, I was completely non-plussed. Children ask the oddest questions. Right out of left field, as our American allies would say. Certainly no one had ever asked me such a question before.

'Makes life *better*?' I repeated.

'Yes,' she said.

'For *other people*?' I thought hard, but absolutely nothing sprang to mind. I tried to think as I spoke. 'There must be a number of things. I mean, that's what one's whole job is about, eighteen hours a day, seven days a week . . .'

Cathy interrupted me as I made the mistake of momentarily drawing breath. She has a future with the BBC, that kid! 'Could you just give me one or two examples, though? Otherwise my article might be a bit boring.'

'Examples. Yes, of course I can,' I said, and found that I couldn't.

Her pencil was poised expectantly above her lined exercise book. I realised that some explanation was called for.

'Well,' I began, 'you see, it's difficult to know where to start. So much of government is collective decisions, all of us together, the best minds in the country hammering it out.'

She seemed dissatisfied with my explanation.

'Yes,' she said doubtfully, 'but what is it you'll look back on afterwards and say "I did that"? You know, like a writer can look at his books.'

Persistent little blighter.

I started to explain the facts of political life. 'Yes, well, politics is a complex business, Cathy.' I was careful to use her name again. 'Lots of people have to have their say. Things take time. Rome wasn't built in a day.'

As I looked at her face, I could see an air of disappointment written across it. [*In view of the insight that Hacker's frequently mixed metaphors give us into the clouded state of his mind, we have retained them unless clarity is threatened. – Ed.*] I began to feel slightly disappointed with myself. I realised that I could not give a proper answer to her question. I also began to feel more than a little irritated that this wretched child should have produced these feelings of inadequacy in me. Enough was enough. It was time to bring the interview to an end.

I pointed out that time was flying, and that I still had to do my boxes.[1] I hustled her out, emphasising how much I'd enjoyed our little talk, and reminding her that she had agreed to let me approve the article before it was printed.

I returned and sat down heavily in my favourite fireside armchair. I was feeling very brought down.

'Bright kid,' commented Annie.

'That's the last time I ever give an interview to a school magazine,' I responded. 'She asked me some very difficult questions.'

'They weren't difficult,' said Annie firmly. 'Just innocent. She was assuming that there is some moral basis to your activities.'

I was puzzled. 'But there is,' I replied.

Annie laughed.

But she didn't just laugh. She laughed till the tears ran down her face, she laughed hopelessly and helplessly. I sat and watched her, becoming more and more confused, trying to laugh with her but

---

[1] The red ministerial dispatch boxes, which contained everything that he had to read, comment on and approve while out of the office.

unable to share the joke. And every time she looked at me she went into another uncontrollable gust of hysteria.

Finally she calmed down, caught her breath, wiped her eyes, and wheezed 'Oh Jim, don't be silly.'

I wasn't amused. I gazed gloomily into the carefully arranged embers of the artificial gas log fire.

'What are you sighing for?' Annie asked.

I tried to explain.

'What *have* I achieved?' I asked. 'Cathy was right.'

Annie suggested that, since Cathy and I had agreed I had all that power, I should go and achieve something forthwith. She *will* persist in making these silly suggestions.

'You know I'm only a Cabinet Minister,' I snapped.

Anne smiled. 'It really does make you humble.'

My humility is not in question, and never has been. The point is that I can't change anything in the foreseeable future. Changing things means getting bills through Parliament, and all the time's been taken up for the next two years.

Annie was unimpressed.

'Why don't you reform the Civil Service?' she suggested.

She makes it sound like one simple little task instead of a lifetime of dedicated carnage. Which reforms in particular did she have in mind, I wondered? Anyway, any real reform of the Civil Service is impossible, as I explained to her.

'Suppose I thought up fifty terrific reforms. Who will have to implement them?'

She saw the point at once. 'The Civil Service,' we said in unison, and she nodded sympathetically. But Annie doesn't give up easily.

'All right,' she suggested, 'not fifty reforms. Just one.'

'One?'

'If you achieve *one* important reform of the Civil Service – that would be something.'

Something? It would get into the *Guinness Book of Records*. I asked her what she was proposing.

'Make them put more women in top civil servants' jobs. Women are half the population. Why shouldn't they be half the Permanent Secretaries? How many women are there at the top?'

I tried to think. Certainly not many. I'd hardly come across any.

'Equal opportunities,' I said. I liked the sound it made. It has a good ring to it, that phrase. 'I'll have a go,' I said. 'Why not? There's a principle at stake.'

13

Annie was delighted. 'You mean you're going to do something out of pure principle?'

I nodded.

'Oh Jim,' she said, with real love and admiration in her voice.

'Principles,' I added, 'are excellent vote-winners.'

Shortly afterwards, Annie developed a headache and went to bed unusually early. I wanted to pursue the conversation with her but she seemed to have lost interest. Odd, that!

June 9th

Today I learned a thing or two about equal opportunities, or the lack of them, in the Civil Service.

Quite coincidentally I had a meeting with Sarah Harrison, who is the only woman Under-Secretary in the DAA.[1]

Sarah really is a splendid person. Very attractive, intelligent, and about thirty-nine or forty-years-old, which is pretty young for an Under-Sec. She has a brisk and – I suppose – slightly masculine approach to meetings and so forth, but seems to be jolly attractive and feminine in spite of all that.

She has brought me a very difficult letter of complaint from one of the opposition front bench on a constituency matter; something to do with special powers for local authorities for land development in special development areas. I had no idea what it all meant or what I was supposed to do about it.

It turned out that I didn't have to do *anything* about it. She explained that some of the facts were wrong, and other points were covered by statutory requirements so that I didn't have any alternatives anyway.

This is the kind of Civil Service advice that makes a Minister's life easy. No decision needed, not even an apology required. Nothing to do at all, in fact. Great.

I asked her to draft a reply, and she'd already done it. She handed it across my desk for me to sign. It was impeccable. I found myself wondering why they don't make more Under-Secretaries like her – and realised that this was the moment to actually *find out*. So I asked her how many women are there at the top of the Civil Service.

She had an immediate answer to that question. 'None of the Permanent Secretaries. Four out of one hundred and fifty odd Deputy Secretaries.'

[1] Department of Administrative Affairs.

I wondered silently if there are any that aren't odd. Presumably not, not by the time they become Deputy Secretaries.

I asked her about her grade – Under-Secretary. As I expected, she knew the precise figure.

'Oh, there's twenty-seven of us.'

That seemed not so bad. 'Out of how many?' I asked.

'Five hundred and seventy-eight.'

I was shocked. Appalled. I wonder why *she* wasn't. At least, she didn't seem to be, she was answering these questions in her usual bright, cheerful, matter-of-fact sort of way.

'Doesn't this appal you?' I asked.

'Not really,' she smiled. 'I think it's comic. But then I think the whole Civil Service is comic. It's run by men, after all.'

As a man who was about to devote himself to the cause of women's rights, I felt able to rise above that one. I was on her side.

'What can you do about it?' I asked. She looked blank. I re-phrased it. 'What can *I* do about it?' I said.

She looked me straight in the eye, with a cool clear gaze. Her eyes were a beautiful deep blue. And she wears an awfully nice perfume.

'Are you serious, Minister?'

I nodded.

'It's easy,' she said. 'Bring top women from the professions and commerce and industry, straight into the top grades. The pay is quite good for women. There's long holidays, index-linked pensions. You'd get a lot of very high-quality applicants.'

'And they could do this job?' I asked.

'Of course.' She seemed surprised at the question.' I mean, with all due respect,[1] if you can make a journalist MP into an instant Minister, why can't you make a senior partner of a top legal firm into an Under-Secretary?' [*Hacker, before he became a Minister, had been a journalist, editing the journal* Reform – *Ed.*] 'Most of the work here only needs about two O-Levels anyway,' she added.

Bernard came in to remind me of my next appointment. He escorted Sarah out. 'Bernard,' I said.

'Yes Minister?' he replied as always. I've been trying to establish a closer personal relationship with him for nearly a year now, why does he persist in such formality?

'I wish you'd call me Jim,' I complained. 'At least when we're alone.'

---

[1] Always an ominous phrase from a civil servant.

He nodded earnestly. 'I'll try to remember that, Minister,' he replied. Hopeless!

I waved the papers from my meeting with Sarah. 'Sarah says this complaint is complete nonsense,' I informed him. 'And she's done a reply.'

Bernard was pleased. 'Fine, we can CGSM it.'

'CGSM?' I asked.

'Civil Service code,' he explained. 'It stands for Consignment of Geriatric Shoe Manufacturers.' I waited for the explanation. 'A load of old cobblers,' he added helpfully.

I took the paper from him.

'I am not a civil servant,' I remarked loftily.' I shall write my own code on it.'

I wrote 'Round Objects' in the margin.

June 11th

Today I had a meeting with Sir Humphrey about equal opportunities. But I had taken care not to let on in advance – in his diary Bernard had written 'Staffing'.

He came in, smiling, confident, benign, patrician, apparently without a care in the world. So I decided to shake him up a bit, then and there.

'Humphrey,' I began, 'I have made a policy decision.'

He froze, half-way down into his chair, in a sort of Groucho Marx position, eyeing me warily with pursed lips.

[*Presumably Hacker intended to say that Sir Humphrey eyed him warily, and that simultaneously he had pursed his lips. – Ed.*]

'A policy decision, Minister?' He recovered himself rapidly and pretended to be pleased with this piece of news.

'Yes,' I replied cheerfully. 'I am going to do something about the number of women in the Civil Service.'

'Surely there aren't all that many?' He looked puzzled.

He was missing the point. Bernard hastened to explain.

'The Minister thinks we need *more*.'

'Many more,' I added firmly.

Now Sir Humphrey really *was* taken aback. His mind was racing. He just couldn't see what I was driving at. 'But we're actually quite well up to Establishment on typists, cleaners, tea-ladies . . .' He petered out, then sought advice. 'Any ideas, Bernard?'

'Well,' said Bernard helpfully, 'we are a bit short of temporary secretaries.'

Clearly Bernard had not got the point either.

'I'm talking about Permanent Secretaries,' I said.

Sir Humphrey was stunned. He seemed unable to formulate a sentence in reply. So I went on.

'We need some female mandarins.' Sir Humphrey was still mentally pole-axed. He didn't respond at all. Bernard also seemed completely baffled. He sought clarification.

'Sort of . . satsumas, Minister?' he enquired desperately.

I'm never quite sure if Bernard has a highly-intelligent deadpan wit, or is faintly moronic. So I told him to sit down.

'How many Permanent Secretaries,' I asked Sir Humphrey, 'are there at the moment?'

'Forty-one, I believe.'

A precise answer.

'Forty-one,' I agreed pleasantly. 'And how many are women?'

Suddenly Sir Humphrey's memory seemed to fail him. 'Well, broadly speaking, not having the exact figures to hand, I'm not exactly sure.'

'Well, approximately?' I encouraged him to reply.

'Well,' he said cautiously, '*approximately* none.'

Close but no cigar, as our American allies would say. *Precisely* none was the correct answer. And Sir Humphrey knew that only too well. [*Hacker was right. The Permanent Secretaries form an exclusive little club in all but name, so exclusive that a newly-nominated Permanent Secretary could, in effect, be blackballed. This would be an 'informal' process not fully clear to their political 'Lords and Masters', but nonetheless effective for all that. – Ed.*]

I was beginning to enjoy myself. 'And I believe there are one hundred and fifty Deputy Secretaries,' I continued gleefully. 'Do you know how many of them are women?'

Sir Humphrey hedged. Either he genuinely didn't know the answer to this one, or wasn't going to say if he did. 'It's difficult to say,' was the best reply he could manage.

This surprised me. 'Why is it difficult?' I wanted to know.

Bernard tried to be helpful again. 'Well, there's a lot of old women among the men.'

I ignored him. 'Four,' I said to Humphrey. 'Four women Dep. Secs. out of one hundred and fifty-three, to be precise.'

Sir Humphrey seemed impressed that there were so many. 'Are there indeed,' he said, slightly wide-eyed.

I had enjoyed my little bit of fun. Now I came bluntly to the point.

17

I had a proposal to make. I've been thinking about it since my first conversation with Sarah.

'I am going to announce,' I announced, 'a quota of twenty-five per cent women Deputy Secretaries and Permanent Secretaries to be achieved within the next four years.'

I think Sir Humphrey was rattled, but it was hard to tell because he's such a smooth operator.

'Minister, I am obviously in total sympathy with your objectives,' he said. This remark naturally increased my suspicions.

'Good,' I said.

'Of course there should be more women at the top. Of *course*. And all of us are deeply concerned by the apparent imbalance.' I noted the skilful use of the word 'apparent'. 'But these things take time.'

I was ready for that one. 'I want to make a start right away,' I replied.

'I agree wholeheartedly,' responded Sir Humphrey enthusiastically. 'And I propose that we make an immediate start by setting up an inter-departmental committee . . .'

This was not what I meant, and he knew it. I told him firmly that I didn't want the usual delaying tactics.

'This needs a sledgehammer,' I declared. 'We must cut through the red tape.'

Bloody Bernard piped up again. 'You can't cut tape with a sledgehammer, it would just . . .' and then he made a sort of squashing gesture. I squashed *him* with a look.

Humphrey seemed upset that I'd accused him of delaying tactics. 'Minister, you do me an injustice,' he complained. 'I was not about to suggest delaying tactics.'

Perhaps I had done him an injustice. I apologised, and waited to see what he *was* about to suggest.

'I was merely going to suggest,' he murmured in a slightly hurt tone, 'that if we are to have a twenty-five per cent quota of women we must have a much larger intake at the recruitment stage. So that eventually we'll have twenty-five per cent in the top jobs.'

'When?' I asked.

I knew the answer before he said it. 'In twenty-five years.'

'No, Humphrey,' I said, still smiling and patient. 'I don't think you've quite got my drift. I'm talking about *now*.'

At last Sir Humphrey got the point. 'Oh,' he said, staggered. 'You mean – *now*!'

'Got it in one, Humphrey,' I replied with my most patronising smile.

'But Minister,' he smiled smoothly, 'it takes time to do things now.' And he smiled patronisingly back at me. It's amazing how quickly he recovers his poise.

I've been hearing that kind of stuff for nearly a year now. It no longer cuts any ice with me. 'Ah yes,' I said, 'the three articles of Civil Service faith: it takes longer to do things quickly, it's more expensive to do things cheaply, and it's more democratic to do things secretly. No Humphrey, I've suggested four years. That's masses of time.'

He shook his head sadly. 'Dear me no, Minister, I don't mean political time, I mean *real* time.' He sat comfortably back in his chair, gazed at the ceiling, and then continued in a leisurely sort of way. 'Civil servants are grown like oak trees, not mustard and cress. They bloom and ripen with the seasons.' I'd never heard such pretentious crap. But he was in full flow. 'They mature like . . .'

'Like you?' I interrupted facetiously.

'I was going to say,' he replied tartly, 'that they mature like an old port.'

'Grimsby, perhaps?'

He smiled a tiny humourless smile. 'I *am* being serious, Minister.'

He certainly was. Apart from being entirely serious about his own importance, he was seriously trying to use all this flim-flam to get me to lose track of my new proposal – or, as I think of it, my new policy decision. I decided to go straight for the jugular.

'I foresaw this problem,' I said firmly. 'So I propose that we solve it by bringing in top women from outside the Service to fill vacancies in the top grades.'

Humphrey's face was a picture. He was absolutely aghast. The colour drained out of his face.

'Minister . . . I don't think I quite . . .' His voice petered out as he reached the word 'understood'.

I was enjoying myself hugely.

'Watch my lips more,' I said helpfully, and pointed to my mouth with my forefinger. 'We . . . will . . . bring . . . women . . . in . . . from . . . out- . . . side!' I said it very slowly and carefully, like a deranged speech therapist. He just sat there and stared at me, transfixed, a rabbit with a snake.

Finally he pulled himself together.

'But,' he began, 'the whole strength of our system is that it is incorruptible, pure, unsullied by outside influences.'

I just can't see the sense in that old chestnut and I said so. 'People move from one job to another throughout industry, Humphrey – why should the Civil Service be different?'

'It *is* different. The Civil Service demands subtlety . . .'

'Discretion,' said Bernard.

'Devotion to duty,' said Humphrey.

'Soundness!' said Bernard.

'*Soundness!*' repeated Sir Humphrey emphatically. 'Well said Bernard. *Soundness.*' Bernard had clearly hit upon one of the key compliments in the Civil Service vocabulary.

[*Bernard Woolley, of course, had an important vested interest in this conversation. If Hacker's policy of bringing women in from outside were implemented, this might well have an adverse effect on the promotion prospects of more junior civil servants such as Woolley. And if women could be brought in to fill top jobs from outside, so could men. What, then, would Bernard Woolley's prospects have been? – Ed.*]

Sir Humphrey went on to explain that civil servants require endless patience and boundless understanding, they need to be able to change horses midstream, constantly, as the politicians change their minds. Perhaps it was my imagination, but it seemed to me that he was putting the word 'minds' in quotes – as if to imply, 'as politicians change what they are pleased to call their minds'.

I asked him if he had all these talents. With a modest shrug he replied: 'Well, it's just that one has been properly . . .'

'Matured,' I interjected. 'Like Grimsby.'

'Trained.' He corrected me with a tight-lipped smile.

'Humphrey,' I said, 'ask yourself honestly if the system is not at fault. *Why* are there so few women Deputy Secretaries?'

'They keep leaving,' he explained, with an air of sweet reason, 'to have babies. And things.'

This struck me as a particularly preposterous explanation, 'Leaving to have babies? At the age of nearly fifty? Surely not!'

But Sir Humphrey appeared to believe it. Desperately he absolved himself of all responsibility or knowledge. 'Really Minister, I don't know. Really I don't. I'm on your side. We do indeed need more women at the top.'

'Good,' I replied decisively, 'because I'm not waiting twenty-five years. We've got a vacancy for a Deputy Secretary here, haven't we?'

He was instantly on his guard. He even thought cautiously for a moment before replying.

'Yes.'

'Very well. We shall appoint a woman. Sarah Harrison.'

Again he was astounded, or aghast, or appalled. Something like that. Definitely not pleased, anyway. But he contented himself with merely repeating her name, in a quiet controlled voice.

'Sarah Harrison?'

'Yes,' I said. 'I think she's very able, don't you?'

'Very able, for a woman. For a person.' He had corrected himself with scarcely a hesitation.

'And,' I added, 'she has ideas. She's an original thinker.'

'I'm afraid that's true,' agreed Sir Humphrey, 'but she doesn't let it interfere with her work.'

So I asked him what he had against her. He insisted that he had *nothing* against her, that he was totally *pro* her. He confirmed that she is an excellent worker, and he pointed out that he is a great supporter of hers and had in fact advocated her promotion to Under-Secretary only last year at a very early age.

'Would you say she is an outstanding Under-Secretary?' I asked him.

'Yes,' he replied, without equivocation.

'So,' I said, 'on balance it's a good idea, isn't it?'

'On balance? Yes . . . and no.'

I told him that that was not a clear answer. He said it was a balanced answer. Touché. Then he went on to explain that the point is, in his opinion, that she's too young and it's not her turn yet.

I leaped upon that argument. I'd been expecting it. 'That is precisely what's *wrong* with the Civil Service – Buggins' Turn! Whereas the best people should be promoted, as soon as possible.'

'Exactly,' agreed Sir Humphrey, 'as soon as it's their turn.'

'Rubbish. Napoleon ruled Europe in his thirties. Alexander the Great conquered the world in his twenties.'

'They would have made *very* poor Deputy Secretaries,' remarked Sir Humphrey contemptuously.

'At least they didn't wait their turn,' I pointed out.

'And look what happened to them.' Sir Humphrey clearly thought he'd won our little debate. So I decided to make the argument rather more personal.

'Look what's happened to *us*,' I said calmly. 'Instead of this country being run by bright energetic youthful brains it is being run by tired routine-bound fifty-five-year-olds who just want a quiet life.'

Humphrey stared at me coldly. 'Had you anyone specific in mind, Minister?'

I smiled. 'Yes . . . and no, Humphrey.' Game, set and match to yours truly, I felt.

Sir Humphrey decided to move the debate back to the specific problem. He informed me, in his most matter-of-fact fashion, that Sarah Harrison is an excellent civil servant and a bright hope for the future. But he also reiterated that she is our most junior Under-Secretary and that he cannot and will not recommend her for promotion.

There was a clear implication in that final comment that it was ultimately up to him, and that I should mind my own business.

I told him he was a sexist.

I'm surprised he didn't laugh at me. Surprisingly, this trendy insult seemed to cut him to the quick. He was outraged.

'Minister,' he complained bitterly, 'how can you say such a thing? I'm very pro-women. Wonderful people, women. And Sarah Harrison is a dear lady. I'm one of her most ardent admirers. But the fact is that if the cause of women is to be advanced it must be done with tact and care and discretion. She is our only woman contender for a top job. We mustn't push her too fast. Women find top jobs very difficult, you know.'

He *is* a sexist.

'Can you hear yourself?' I asked incredulously.

Unabashed, he continued in the same vein. 'If women were able to be good Permanent Secretaries, there would be more of them, wouldn't there? Stands to reason.'

I've never before heard a reply that so totally begs the question.

'No Humphrey!' I began, wondering where to begin.

But on he went. 'I'm no anti-feminist. I love women. Some of my best friends are women. My wife, indeed.' Methinks Sir Humphrey doth protest too much. And on and on he went. 'Sarah Harrison is not very experienced, Minister, and her two children are still of school age, they might get mumps.'

Another daft argument. Anybody can be temporarily off work through their own ill-health, not just their children's. 'You might get shingles, Humphrey, if it comes to that,' I said.

He missed my point. 'I might indeed Minister, if you continue in this vein,' he muttered balefully. 'But what if her children caused her to miss work all the time?'

I asked him frankly if this were likely. I asked if she were likely to have reached the rank of Under-Secretary if her children kept having mumps. I pointed out that she was the best person for the job.

He didn't disagree about that. But he gave me an indignant warning: 'Minister, if you go around promoting women just because they're the best person for the job, you could create a lot of resentment throughout the whole Civil Service.'

'But not from the women in it,' I pointed out.

'Ah,' said Sir Humphrey complacently, 'but there are so few of them that it wouldn't matter so much.'

A completely circular argument. Perhaps this is what is meant by moving in Civil Service circles.

[*Later in the week Sir Humphrey Appleby had lunch with Sir Arnold Robinson, the Cabinet Secretary, at the Athenaeum Club. Sir Humphrey, as always, made a note on one of his long thin pieces of memo paper simulating a margin. – Ed.*]

Arnold's feelings are the same as mine when it comes to women. We both like them well enough, in their way. But like me – and unlike the Minister – he sees quite clearly that they are different from us. In the following ways:–

1. *Bad for teamwork:* they put strains on a team, by reacting differently from us.
2. *Too emotional:* They are not rational like us.
3. *Can't be Reprimanded:* They either get into a frightful bate or start blubbing.
4. *Can be Reprimanded:* Some of them can be, but are frightfully hard and butch and not in the least bit attractive.

5. *Prejudices:* They are full of them.

6. *Silly Generalisations:* They make them.

7. *Stereotypes:* They think in them.

I asked Arnold for his advice. Arnold suggested that I lecture the Minister at such length on the matter that he becomes bored and loses interest in the whole idea.

There is a remote chance of success for such a plan. But Hacker does not get bored easily. He even finds *himself* interesting. They all do in fact. All the ones who listen to what they're saying of course. On second thoughts, that is by no means all of them.

But the fact remains that Hacker's boredom threshold is high. He even reads most of the stuff that we put into his red boxes, with apparent interest!

Arnold also suggested that standard second ploy: to tell the Minister that the Unions won't wear it. [*'It' being the importation of women into the Service to fill some top jobs. – Ed.*] We agreed that this was a line of action worth pursuing.

We also discussed the feminine angle. His wife is in favour of promoting the Harrison female, and may well – from what I know of Mrs H. – be behind all this. However, she may not know that Harrison is extremely attractive. I'm sure Mrs H. and Mrs H. have never met. This could well be fruitful.

I pointed out that the Cabinet will be in favour of Hacker's proposal. But we agreed that we could doubtless get the Cabinet to change their minds. They change their minds fairly easily. Just like a lot of women. Thank God they don't blub.

[*Appleby Papers 37/6PJ/457*].

[*It is interesting to compare Sir Humphrey's self-confident account of this luncheon with the notes made by Sir Arnold Robinson on Sir Humphrey's report, which were found among the Civil Service files at Walthamstow. – Ed.*]

Told Appleby that I wasn't impressed with his Minister's plan to bring in women from outside, novel though the idea may be

[*'Wasn't impressed' would be an example of Civil Service understatement. Readers may imagine the depth of feeling behind such a phrase. The use of the Civil Service killer word 'novel' is a further indication of Sir Arnold's hostility. – Ed.*]

Suggested that he bore the Minister out of the idea. Appleby claimed that this would not work. Probably correct.

So I made various other suggestions. For instance, the Trade Union ploy: suggesting to the Minister that the Unions won't wear it. Appleby missed the point completely. He told me that the Unions would like it. He's probably right, but it was completely beside the point!

I also suggested pointing the Minister's wife in the right direction. And suggested that we try to ensure that the Cabinet throws it out. Appleby agreed to try all these plans. But I am disturbed that he had thought of none of them himself.

Must keep a careful eye on H.A. Is early retirement a possibility to be discussed with the PM.?

A.R.

Staff Report (Cont.)   CR36

---

7. LONG TERM POTENTIAL

At present, he/~~she~~ seems

unlikely to progress further	☑ 1
or to have potential to rise about one grade but probably no further	☐ 2
or to have potential to rise two or three grades	☐ 3
or to have exceptional potential	☐ 4

8. GENERAL REMARKS

Please provide any additional relevant information here, drawing attention to any particular strengths or weaknesses.

Told Appleby that I wasn't impressed with his Minister's plan to bring in women from outside, novel though the idea may be.

Suggested that he bore the Minister out of the idea. Appleby claimed that this would not work. Probably correctly.

So I made various other suggestions. For instance, the Trade Union ploy: suggesting to the Minister that the Unions won't wear it. Appleby missed the point completely. He told me that the Unions would like it. He's probably right, but it was completely beside the point!

[*Naturally, Sir Humphrey never saw these notes, because no civil servant is ever shown his report except in wholly exceptional circumstances.*

And equally naturally, Hacker never knew of the conversation between Sir Arnold and Sir Humphrey over luncheon at the Athenaeum.

It was in this climate of secrecy that our democracy used to operate. Civil servants' word for secrecy was 'discretion'. They argued that discretion was the better part of valour. – Ed.]

[Hacker's diary continues – Ed.]
June 16th
Sir Humphrey walked into my office today, sat down and made the most startling remark that I have yet heard from him.

'Minister,' he said, 'I have come to the conclusion that you were right.'
finally, after nearly a year, it seemed that he was beginning to take me seriously.

However, I was immediately suspicious, and I asked him to amplify his remark. I had not the least idea to which matter he was referring. Of course, asking Humphrey to amplify his remarks is often a big mistake.

'I am fully-seized of your ideas and have taken them on board and I am now positively against discrimination against women and positively in favour of positive discrimination in their favour – discriminating discrimination of course.'

I think it was something like that. I got the gist of it anyway.

Then he went on, to my surprise: 'I understand a view is forming at the very highest level that this should happen.' I think he must have been referring to the PM. Good news.

Then, to my surprise he asked why the matter of equal opportunities for women should not apply to politics as well as the Civil Service. I was momentarily confused. But he explained that there are only twenty-three women MPs out of a total of six hundred and fifty. I agreed that this too is deplorable, but, alas, there is nothing at all that we can do about that.

He remarked that these figures were an indication of discrimination against women by the political parties. Clearly, he argued, the way they select candidates is fundamentally discriminatory.

I found myself arguing in defence of the parties. It was a sort of reflex action. 'Yes and no,' I agreed. 'You know, it's awfully difficult for women to be MPs – long hours, debates late at night, being away from home a lot. Most women have a problem with that and with homes, and husbands.'

'And mumps,' he added helpfully.

I realised that he was sending me up. And simultaneously trying to suggest that I too am a sexist. An absurd idea, of course, and I told him so in no uncertain terms.

I steered the discussion towards specific goals and targets. I asked what we would do to start implementing our plan.

Humphrey said that the first problem would be that the unions won't agree to this quota.

I was surprised to hear this, and immediately suggested that we get them in to talk about it.

This suggestion made him very anxious. 'No, no, no,' he said. 'No. That would stir up a hornet's nest.'

I couldn't see why. Either Humphrey was paranoid about the unions – or it was just a ploy to frighten me. I suspect the latter. [*Hacker was now learning fast. – Ed.*]

The reason I suspect a trick is that he offered no explanation as to why he shouldn't talk to the union leaders. Instead he went off on an entirely different tack.

'If I might suggest we be realistic about this . . .' he began.

I interrupted. 'By realistic, do you mean drop the whole scheme?'

'No!' he replied vehemently. 'Certainly not! But perhaps a pause to regroup, a lull in which we reassess the position and discuss alternative strategies, a space of time for mature reflection and deliberation . . .'

I interrupted again. 'Yes, you mean drop the whole scheme.' This time I wasn't asking a question. And I dealt with the matter with what I consider to be exemplary firmness. I told him that I had set my hand to the plough and made my decision. 'We shall have a twenty-five per cent quota of women in the open structure in four years from now. And to start with I shall promote Sarah Harrison to Dep. Sec.'

He was frightfully upset. 'No Minister!' he cried in vain, 'I'm sure that's the wrong decision.'

This was quite a remarkable reaction from the man who had begun the meeting by telling me that I was absolutely right.

I emphasised that I could not be moved on this matter because it is a matter of principle. I added that I shall have a word with my cabinet colleagues, who are bound to support me as there are a lot of votes in women's rights.

'I thought you said it was a matter of principle, Minister, not of votes.'

He was being too clever by half. I was able to explain, loftily, that I was referring to my cabinet colleagues. For me it *is* a matter of principle.

A very satisfactory meeting. I don't think he can frustrate me on this one.

June 17th

Had a strange evening out with Annie. She collected me from the office at five-thirty, because we had to go to a Party drinks 'do' at Central House.[1]

I had to keep her waiting a while because my last meeting of the day ran late, and I had a lot of letters to sign.

Signing letters, by the way, is an extraordinary business because there are so many of them. Bernard lays them out in three or four long rows, all running the full length of my conference table – which seats twelve a side. Then I whizz along the table, signing the letters as I go. It's quicker to move me than them. As I go Bernard collects the signed letters up behind me, and moves a letter from the second row to replace the signed and collected one in the first row. Then I whizz back along the table, signing the next row.

I don't actually read them all that carefully. It shows the extent of my trust for Bernard. Sometimes I think that I might sign absolutely anything if I were in a big enough hurry.

Bernard had an amusing bit of news for me today.

'You remember that letter you wrote "Round objects" on?' he asked.

'Yes.'

'Well,' he said with a slight smile, 'it's come back from Sir Humphrey's office. He commented on it.'

And he showed me the letter. In the margin Humphrey had written: 'Who is Round and to what does he object?'

Anyway, I digress. While all this signing was going on, Annie was given a sherry by Humphrey in his office. I thought it was jolly nice of him to take the trouble to be sociable when he could have been on the 5.59 for Haslemere. Mind you, I think he likes Annie and anyway perhaps he thinks it's politic to chat up the Minister's wife.

But, as I say, Annie and I had a strange evening. She seemed rather cool and remote. I asked her if anything was wrong, but she wouldn't say what. Perhaps she resented my keeping her waiting so long, because I know she finds Humphrey incredibly boring. Still, that's the penalty you have to pay if you're married to a successful man.

[*A note in Sir Humphrey's diary reveals the true cause of Mrs Hacker's disquiet. – Ed.*]

[1] Hacker's Party HQ.

Friday 17 JUNE

Had a sherry with Mrs Hacker this evening. The Minister was delayed signing letters, which was not entirely coincidental. Naturally I had taken care to ensure that his previous meeting overran somewhat.

I brought the conversation around to the matter of changing and reforming the Civil Service. As expected, she was pretty keen on the whole idea.

Had a sherry with Mrs Hacker this evening. The Minister was delayed signing letters, which was not entirely coincidental. Naturally I had taken care to ensure that his previous meeting overran somewhat.

I brought the conversation around to the matter of changing and reforming the Civil Service. As expected, she was pretty keen on the whole idea.

Immediately she asked me about the promotion of the Harrison female. 'What about promoting this woman that Jim was talking about?'

I talked about it all with great enthusiasm. I said that the Minister certainly has an eye for talent. I said that Sarah was undoubtedly very talented. And thoroughly delightful. A real charmer.

I continued for many minutes in the same vein. I said how much I admired this new generation of women civil servants compared with the old battle-axes of yesteryear. I said that naturally most of the new generation aren't as beautiful as Sarah, but they all are thoroughly feminine.

Mrs Hacker was becoming visibly less enthusiastic about Sarah Harrison's promotion, minute by minute. She remarked that Hacker had never discussed what Sarah looked like.

I laughed knowingly. I said that perhaps he hadn't noticed, though that would be pretty hard to believe. I laid it on pretty thick – made her sound like a sort of administrative Elizabeth Taylor. I said that no man could fail to notice how attractive she was, *especially* the Minister, as he spends such a considerable amount of time with her. And will spend even more if she's promoted.

My feeling is that the Minister will get no further encouragement from home on this matter.

[*Appleby Papers 36/RJC/471*]

[*Sir Arnold Robinson and Sir Humphrey Appleby were plainly quite confident, as we have already seen, that they could sway a sufficient number of Hacker's cabinet colleagues to vote against this proposal when it came before them.*

The source of their confidence was the practice, current in the 1970s and 1980s, of holding an informal meeting of Permanent Secretaries on Wednesday mornings. This meeting took place in the office of the Cabinet Secretary, had no agenda and was – almost uniquely among Civil Service meetings – unminuted.

Permanent Secretaries would 'drop in' and raise any question of mutual interest. This enabled them all to be fully-briefed about any matters that were liable to confront their Ministers in Cabinet, which took place every Thursday morning i.e. the next day. And it gave them time to give their Ministers encouragement or discouragement as they saw fit on particular issues.

Fortunately Sir Humphrey's diary reveals what occurred at the Permanent Secretaries' meeting that fateful Wednesday morning. – Ed.]

I informed my colleagues that my Minister is intent on creating a quota of twenty-five per cent women in the open structure, leading to an eventual fifty per cent. Parity, in other words.

Initially, my colleagues' response was that it was an interesting suggestion.

[*'Interesting' was another Civil Service form of abuse, like 'Novel' or, worse still, 'Imaginative'. – Ed.*]

Arnold set the tone for the proper response. His view was that it is right and proper that men and women be treated fairly and equally. In principle we should all agree, he said, that such targets should be set and goals achieved.

Everyone agreed immediately that we should agree in principle to such an excellent idea, that it was right and proper to set such targets and achieve such goals.

Arnold then canvassed several of my colleagues in turn, to see if they could implement this excellent proposal in their departments.

Bill [*Sir William Carter, Permanent Secretary at the Foreign and Commonwealth Office. – Ed.*] said that he was in full agreement, naturally. He believes that the Civil Service must institute some positive discrimination in favour of women. But regretfully he felt obliged to point out that it cannot happen in the FCO for obvious reasons. Clearly we cannot post women ambassadors to Iran, or any of the Muslim countries, for instance. Generally speaking most of the Third World countries are not as advanced as we are in connection with women's rights – and as we have to send our diplomats to new postings every three years, and entertain many Islamic VIPs in this country, the proposal would definitely not work for the FCO.

Nonetheless he wished to make it clear that he applauded the principle.

Ian [*Sir Ian Simpson, Permanent Secretary of the Home Office. – Ed.*] said that he was enthusiastically in favour of the principle. He believes we all could benefit from the feminine touch. Furthermore, women are actually *better* at handling some problems than men. He had no doubt about this. Regretfully, however, an exception would have to be made in the case of the Home Office: women are not the right people to run prisons, or the police. And quite probably, they wouldn't want to do it anyway.

We all agreed that this was probably so.

Peter [*Sir Peter Wainwright, Permanent Secretary of the Department of Defence. – Ed.*] said that, alas! the same applies to Defence. Women are hardly the people to control all those admirals and generals. Nor is it a practical possibility to place a woman at the Head of Security.

I observed that M. would have to become F. This provoked a gratifying degree of merriment around the table.

Arnold, speaking for us all, agreed that Defence must clearly be a man's world. Like Industry. And Employment, with all those trade union barons to cope with.

John [*Sir John McKendrick, Permanent Secretary of the Department of Health and Social Security. – Ed.*] took an even more positive line. He was happy to inform us that women are already well represented near the top of the DHSS, which has two of the four women Dep. Secs. currently in Whitehall. Neither of them is in line for Permanent Secretary, obviously, as they are Deputy Chief Medical Officers, (and in any case they may not be suitable for other reasons). Furthermore, women constitute eighty per cent of the typing grades, so he was delighted to be able to tell us that his Department is not doing too badly by them. He added that, in principle, he was in favour of them going to the very top.

Arnold summed up all the views expressed: the feeling of the meeting was – unquestionably – that in principle we were all thoroughly in favour of equal rights for the ladies. It is just that there are special problems in individual departments.

I raised again the question of the quota and stated that I was against it.

Everyone immediately supported me. There was a feeling that it was not on and a bad idea – in fact a typical politician's idea.

I gave my view: namely, that we must always have the right to promote the best man for the job, regardless of sex.

Furthermore – and I made it clear that I was speaking as an ardent feminist myself – I pointed out that the problem lay in recruiting the right sort of women. Married women with families tend to drop out because, in all honesty, they cannot give their work their full single-minded attention. And unmarried women with no children are not fully-rounded people with a thorough understanding of life.

There was general agreement that family life was essential and that it was hard for spinsters to be fully-rounded individuals.

I summed up my remarks by saying that, in practice, it is rarely possible to find a fully-rounded married woman with a happy home and three children who is prepared to devote virtually her whole life, day and night, to a Government Department. It's Catch 22 – or, rather, Catch 22, subparagraph (a).

Arnold had allowed considerable time for this discussion, which indicates the importance that he attached to the problem. He concluded the matter by asking everyone present to ensure that all of their respective Ministers oppose the quota idea in Cabinet by seeing that each Minister's attention is drawn to each Department's own special circumstances. But he also asked all present to be sure to recommend the *principle* of equal opportunities at every level.

Through the chair, I made one final point. My Minister sees the promotion of women as one means of achieving greater diversity at the top of the Service. I asked all my colleagues to stress, when briefing their Ministers, that quite frankly one could not find a more diverse collection of people than us.

It was unanimously agreed that we constitute a real cross-section of the nation.

[*Appleby Papers – 41/AAG/583*].

[Hacker's diary continues – Ed.]
June 19th

Cabinet today. And with a very odd outcome. I put forward my proposal for a quota for women for top Civil Service jobs.

All my Cabinet colleagues agreed *in principle* but then they all went on to say that it wouldn't work in their particular Departments. So in the end they didn't really support me at all.

Curiously enough, I'm no longer getting the support from Annie that I was. Not about the quota, specifically, but about promoting Sarah. I had expected her to be *at least* one hundred per cent behind it. But she goes all distant when I talk about it. In fact, she seems to be dead against it now. Extraordinary.

However, as the quota policy is now in ruins it seems that Sarah's promotion is the only thing left that I can immediately achieve in this area. I have arranged that Humphrey and I speak to her tomorrow. I am determined to push it through.

June 20th

My whole equal opportunities policy is destroyed, and quite frankly I feel pretty bitter about the whole thing in general and women in particular. Or at least one particular woman in particular.

Before I saw Sarah today I told Humphrey that we at least could make one tiny positive step today. Lighting a spark.

'Carrying a torch, even,' he replied. What was that supposed to mean?

Anyway, Sarah came in. I explained the background to her: that we have a vacancy for a Deputy Secretary in a Department and that, in spite of her being the most junior of our Under-Secs but because she is the outstanding person in her grade, we were happy to be able to tell her that Humphrey and I were recommending her for promotion to the rank of Deputy Secretary.

Her reaction was a little surprising.

'Oh,' she said. 'I don't know what to say.' And then she laughed.

I couldn't imagine what she was laughing at.

'You don't have to say anything,' I said.

'A single thank you should suffice,' said Humphrey.

She was still smiling. Then she dropped the bombshell. 'No – I mean – oh gosh! Look, this is awfully embarrassing – I mean, well, I was going to tell you this week – the fact is I'm resigning from the Civil Service.'

You could have knocked me down with a feather. And Humphrey too, by the look of him.

I said something brilliantly witty and apposite, like 'What?', and Humphrey gasped 'resigning?'

'Yes,' she said. 'So thank you, but no thank you.'

Humphrey asked if there was some problem with her children at home.

Bernard suggested mumps.

I suggested that Bernard shut up.

Sarah said she was joining a merchant bank. As a Director.

She'll earn more than me. Perhaps even more than Humphrey!

I tried to explain to her that this news was a frightful blow. 'You see, Sarah, the reason that I'm telling you of your promotion – or rather, Humphrey and I together – is that I have been fighting a losing battle to improve the promotion prospects of women at the top of the Service. And, well, you were to be my Trojan Horse.'

She then explained the reason for her move. 'Quite honestly Minister, I want a job where I don't spend endless hours circulating information that isn't relevant about subjects that don't matter to people who aren't interested. I want a job where there is achievement rather than merely activity. I'm tired of pushing paper. I would like to be able to point at something and say "I did that."'

The irony of what she was saying was extraordinary. I understand her feeling only too well.

Sir Humphrey didn't. He looked blank. 'I don't understand,' he said.

She smiled. 'I know. That's why I'm leaving.'

I explained that I *did* understand. But I asked her if she was saying that governing Britain is unimportant.

'No,' she said, 'it's very important. It's just that I haven't met anyone who's doing it.'

She added that she'd had enough of the pointless intrigue. I asked what she had in mind. 'Your using me as a Trojan Horse, for instance. And they probably told you that the unions wouldn't wear it if you promoted me.'

I was staggered. Had there been a leak? I asked her how she knew.

She was delighted. She grinned from ear to ear. 'Oh *I didn't* know. I just know how things are done here.'

We both stared at Humphrey, who had the grace to look slightly embarrassed.

I made one last effort to persuade her to change her mind. 'Look here Sarah,' I said sternly, 'you don't seem to appreciate that I've fought quite a battle for you.'

Suddenly her eyes blazed. For the first time I recognised the toughness that had brought her to near the top. And the sense of style and dignity. I realised that I'd said something awfully wrong.

'Oh, have you?' she asked. 'Well, I didn't ask you to fight a battle for me. I'm not pleased at the idea of being part of a twenty-five per cent quota. Women are not inferior beings, and I don't enjoy being patronised. I'm afraid you're as paternalist and chauvinist as the rest of them. I'm going somewhere where I shall be accepted as an equal, on my own merits, as a person.'

I was speechless. Clearly I'd offended her. And I suddenly realised that you can't win.

'May I go now?'

There was, of course, no reason to keep her sitting there. I apologised for offending her, though I couldn't see how I'd done it.

'No,' she said, in a kindly way. 'And thank you – I know you both *mean* well.' And off she went, leaving two very puzzled and deflated chaps.

'Women!' I said.

'Yes Minister,' murmured Humphrey, nodding sadly as if to say 'I told you so!'

[*This was not quite the end of the matter. Recently published papers revealed that Hacker fought on for his twenty-five per cent quota for some considerable time – some weeks, anyway. And, as Sir*

Harold Wilson once said, a week is a long time in politics.

Sir Humphrey's ingenuity rose to the occasion. He warned Hacker that the Race Relations Board had heard on the grapevine of his proposed quota for women. He told Hacker that if there was to be any affirmative action within the Civil Service, there must also be a quota of blacks within the Civil Service. Humphrey explained that there was a principle at stake.

Hacker was less than enthusiastic about this new principle. He was certainly not a racist, but he could see clearly that whereas a quota for women was a vote-winner, a quota for blacks was in all probability a vote-loser.

Some days later Hacker raised what he called 'this whole business of minority groups – women, blacks, trade unionists and so forth.'

Sir Humphrey explained to Hacker that women and trade unionists were not minority groups, even though they share the same paranoia which is the hallmark of any minority group.

So finally Hacker proposed what Appleby had always proposed: namely, that they start by creating equal opportunities for both women and blacks. In the recruitment grades.

And they drew up terms of reference for an inter-departmental committee to report on methods of choosing the right individuals to be civil servants, to report four years hence. By which time Hacker would certainly no longer be the Minister. – Ed.]

2
The
Challenge

June 24th

Wonderful news today. I had a call at home last night to go straight to Number Ten this morning.

When I got there I was told of a big Government administrative reorganisation. Not a reshuffle; I stay Minister of Administrative Affairs at the DAA. But I've been given a new remit: local government. It's quite a challenge.

[*Later that day Hacker was interviewed by Ludovic Kennedy in* The World At One, *a popular radio current affairs programme in the 1970s and 80s.*

We have obtained a transcript of the broadcast discussion, which we reproduce below. – Ed]

BBC Radio

```
LUDOVIC:    And the main news this Thursday p.m. is the

government reorganisation which gives an ever-increasing

empire to the Minister for Administrative Affairs, the Right

Honourable James Hacker MP.  It has been said, Mr Hacker,

that you are now Mr Town Hall as well as Mr Whitehall?

HACKER:    Well, it's awfully flattering of you to put it

that way, Ludo ...

LUDOVIC:    It wasn't me who put it that way, Mr Hacker,

it was the Daily Mirror.  I was merely seeking confirmation

that you are now this country's chief bureaucrat.
```

B B C Radio

HACKER: I see. Well, of course, that's nonsense. This government believes in reducing bureaucracy.

LUDOVIC: Figures I have here say that your Department's staff has risen by ten per cent this year.

HACKER: Certainly not.

LUDOVIC: Well, what figure do you have?

HACKER: I believe the latest figure was more like 9.97%.

LUDOVIC: You see, it has been suggested, Mr Hacker, that your department is engaged less in reducing bureaucracy than in increasing it.

HACKER: Yes, but that's only because we've had to take on staff in order to reduce staff.

LUDOVIC: I beg your pardon?

HACKER: It's commonsense. You have to take on more doctors to cure more patients. You have to take on more firemen to extinguish more fires. You have to...

LUDOVIC: (INTERRUPTION) And how do you propose to extinguish local government bureaucracy?

HACKER: Well, it's a challenge, and I'm looking forward to it.

LUDOVIC: Would you agree that there's even more bureaucratic waste there than in Whitehall?

HACKER: Well, yes, that's what makes it a challenge.

LUDOVIC: And how are you going to meet this challenge?

Cont.

BBC Radio

HACKER: Ah, well, it's too early to announce detailed proposals. After all, I've come here direct from Number Ten.

LUDOVIC: You mean Number 9.97?

HACKER: The broad principle is to cut ruthlessly at waste while preserving services intact...

LUDOVIC: That's just what your predecessor said when he was appointed. Do you mean he's failed?

HACKER: Please let me finish. Because we must be absolutely clear about this. And I want to be quite frank with you. The plain fact of the matter is, that, at the end of the day, it is the right - nay, the duty - of the elected government, in the House of Commons, to ensure that government policy, the policies on which we were elected and for which we have a mandate, the policies for which the people voted, are the policies which, finally, when the national cake has been divided up - and, may I remind you, we as a nation don't have unlimited wealth, you know, we can't pay ourselves more than we've earned - are the policies ... er, what was the question again?

LUDOVIC: I was asking if you would agree that your immediate predecessor was a failure?

HACKER: No, on the contrary, quite the reverse, it's just that this job is a really enormous, er...

LUDOVIC: Challenge?

HACKER: Exactly.

[*The following day Sir Humphrey Appleby received a note from Sir Arnold Robinson, Secretary to the Cabinet. We reproduce below the exchange of notes that ensued. – Ed.*]

10 DOWNING STREET

From the Secretary to the Cabinet

June 25th.

Dear Humphy,

　　Heard your chap on the radio yesterday. Sounded as though he wanted to <u>do</u> things about your new Local Government remit. Kept calling it a challenge.

　　I do want you to be quite clear in your own mind that I wouldn't have given you Local Government if I thought you were going to let Hacker do anything about it.

A.

The reply from Sir Humphrey Appleby:

**MINISTRY OF
ADMINISTRATIVE AFFAIRS**

From the Permanent Under Secretary of State

Dear Arnold : —

I'm sure he won't be able to.

Nobody else has.

HA

26/vi

A reply from Sir Arnold Robinson:

10 DOWNING STREET

From the Secretary to the Cabinet

June 27th

Dear Humphy,

That's not the point. We have found in the past that all Local Government reforms rebound on us. Whenever anybody finds a way of saving money or cutting staff in Local Government, you will find it works for Whitehall just as well.

If he needs something to keep him busy get him to look into Civil Defence.

A.

[On the same date, 27 June, Sir Humphrey made a reference to this exchange of notes in his diary. – Ed.]

Received a couple of notes from A.R. Clearly he's worried that Hacker may overstep the mark. I've made it plain that I know my duty.

Nonetheless, A. made a superb suggestion: that I divert Hacker by getting him to look into Civil Defence. By which he means fall-out shelters.

This is a most amusing notion. Everybody knows that Civil Defence is not a serious issue, merely a desperate one. And it is thus best left to those whose incapacity can be relied upon: local authorities.

It is a hilarious thought that, since the highest duty of government is to protect its citizens, it has been decided to leave it to the Borough Councils.

[Hacker's diary continues – Ed.]
June 30th

I met a very interesting new advisor today: Dr Richard Cartwright.

We were having a meeting of assorted officials, of which he was one. I noticed that we hadn't even been properly introduced to each other, which I had presumed was some sort of oversight.

But, as the meeting was breaking up, this shambling figure of an elderly schoolboy placed himself directly in front of me and asked me in a soft Lancashire accent if he could have a brief word with me.

Naturally I agreed. Also, I was intrigued. He looked a bit different from most of my officials – a baggy tweed sports jacket, leather elbows, mousey hair brushed forward towards thick spectacles. He looked like a middle-aged ten-year-old. If I'd tried to guess his profession, I would have guessed prep. school science master.

'It's about a proposal, worked out before we were transferred to this Department,' he said in his comforting high-pitched voice.

'And you are . . .?' I asked. I still didn't know who he was.

'I am . . . what?' he asked me.

I thought he was going to tell me what his job is. 'Yes,' I asked, 'you are what?'

He seemed confused. 'What?'

Now I was confused. 'What?'

'I'm Dr Cartwright.'

Bernard chose this moment to intervene. 'But if I may put it another way . . . what *are* you?'

'I'm C of E,' said Dr Cartwright puzzled.

'No,' said Bernard patiently. 'I think the Minister means, what function do you perform in this Department.'

'Don't you *know*?' Dr Cartwright sounded slightly horrified.

'Yes, *I* know,' said Bernard, 'but the Minister wants to know.'

'Ah,' said Dr Cartwright. We'd got there at last. No one would believe that this is how busy people in the corridors of power communicate with each other.

'I'm a professional economist,' he explained. 'Director of Local Administrative Statistics.'

'So you were in charge of the Local Government Directorate until we took it over?'

He smiled at my question. 'Dear me, no.' He shook his head sadly, though apparently without bitterness. 'No, I'm just Under-Secretary rank. Sir Gordon Reid was the Permanent Secretary. I fear that I will rise no higher.'

I asked why not.

He smiled. 'Alas! I am an expert.'

[*It is interesting to note that the cult of the generalist had such a grip on Whitehall that experts accepted their role as second-class citizens with equanimity and without rancour. – Ed.*]

'An expert on what?'

'The whole thing,' he said modestly. Then he handed me a file.

I'm sitting here reading the file right now. It's dynamite. It's a scheme for controlling local authority expenditure. He proposes that every council official responsible for a new project would have to list the criteria for failure before he's given the go-ahead.

I didn't grasp the implication of this at first. But I've discussed it with Annie and she tells me it's what's called 'the scientific method'. I've never really come across that, since my early training was in sociology and economics. But 'the scientific method' apparently means that you first establish a method of measuring the success or failure of an experiment. A proposal would have to say: 'The scheme will be a failure if it takes longer than this' or 'costs more than that' or 'employs more staff than these' or 'fails to meet those pre-set performance standards'.

Fantastic. We'll get going on this right away. The only thing is, I can't understand why this hasn't been done before.

July 1st

The first thing I did this morning was get Dr Cartwright on the phone, and ask him.

He didn't know the answer. 'I can't understand it either. I put the idea up several times and it was always welcomed very warmly. But Sir Gordon always seemed to have something more urgent on when we were due to discuss it.'

43

I told him he'd come to the right place this time and rang off.

Then Bernard popped in. He was looking rather anxious. Obviously he'd been listening-in on his extension and taking notes. [*This was customary, and part of the Private Secretary's official duties. – Ed.*]

'That's marvellous isn't it Bernard?' I asked.

There was a pointed silence.

'You've read the report, have you? Cartwright's report?'

'Yes, Minister.'

'Well, what do you think of it?'

'Oh, it's er, that is, er it's very well presented, Minister.'

The message was clear.

'Humphrey will be fascinated, don't you think?' I said mischievously.

Bernard cleared his throat. 'Well, I've arranged a meeting with him about this for tomorrow. I'm sure he'll give you his views.'

'What are you saying, Bernard? Out with it.'

'Yes, well, as I say,' he waffled for a bit, 'um . . . I think that he'll think that it's er, beautifully . . . typed.'

And then surprisingly he smiled from ear to ear.

July 2nd

Today I had the meeting with Sir Humphrey. It was supposed to be about our new responsibilties in the area of local government. But I saw to it that it was about Cartwright's scheme.

It began with the usual confusion between us.

'Local authorities,' I began. 'What are we going to do about them?'

'Well, there are three principal areas for action: budget, accommodation and staffing.'

I congratulated him for putting his finger right on it. 'Well done, Humphrey. That's where all the trouble is.'

He was nonplussed. 'Trouble?'

'Yes,' I said, 'with all those frightful councils. Budget, accommodation and staffing. They all go up and up and up.'

'No, Minister.' He had assumed his patronising tone again. 'I'm afraid you misunderstand. I'm referring to this Department's budget, accommodation and staffing. Obviously they must all be increased now that we have all those extra responsibilities.'

I was even *more* patronising in my response. 'No Humphrey, I'm afraid *you* misunderstand.' I told him that local government is a ghastly mess, and that I was asking what we were going to do to improve it, to make it more efficient and economical.

He didn't answer my question. He hesitated momentarily, and then tried to divert me with flattery. 'Minister, this new remit gives you more influence, more Cabinet seniority – but you do not have to let it give you any more work or worry. That would be foolishness.'

Nowadays I find I'm able to resist his blandishments very easily. Stubbornly I repeated that we have to put a stop to all this ghastly waste and extravagance that's going on.

'Why?' he asked.

I was staggered. 'Why?'

'Yes. Why?'

'Because it's my job, we're the government, we were elected to govern.'

'Minister, surely you don't intend to tamper with the democratic rights of freely-elected local government representatives?'

Humphrey's new-found interest in democracy surprised me slightly. For a moment I couldn't think of an answer to what sounded like a perfectly reasonable point. And then it became clear. There is *no* competition between local government and Westminster – local authorities are given their powers by Westminster. They must act accordingly. Parliament is supreme. We live in a Parliamentary democracy. And there was another aspect to this.

'Local councils aren't democratic at all,' I said. 'Local democracy is a farce. Nobody knows who their local councillor is. Most people don't even vote in local elections. And the ones who *do*, just treat it as a popularity poll on the government in Westminster. Councillors, in practice, are accountable to nobody.'

He looked po-faced. 'They are public-spirited citizens, selflessly sacrificing their spare time.'

'Have you ever met any?' I enquired.

'Occasionally. When there was no alternative,' he replied, with one of his occasional flashes of honesty.

'I've met plenty of them. Half of them are self-important busy-bodies on an ego trip and the other half are in it for what they can get out of it.'

'Perhaps they ought to be in the House of Commons,' said Humphrey.

I think I must have given him a dirty look, because he added hastily, 'I mean, to see how a proper legislative assembly behaves.'

I decided that we'd done enough beating about the bush. I told

45

Humphrey that I intended to get a grip on these local councils. And I announced that I had a plan.

He smiled a supercilious smile. '*You* have a plan?'

I told him that I was going to insist that any council official who puts up a project costing over £10,000 must accompany it with failure standards.

'With what?'

'With a statement,' I said, 'that he will have failed if his project does not achieve certain pre-set results or exceeds fixed time or staff or budget limits.'

I had hoped, faintly, that he would think this was my idea. No such luck.

'Minister,' he demanded, 'where did you get the idea for this dangerous nonsense?'

I could see that Dr Cartwright needed my protection. 'From someone in the Department,' I replied evasively.

He exploded. 'Minister, I have warned you before about the dangers of talking to people in the Department. I *implore* you to stay out of the minefield of local government. It is a political graveyard.'

Bernard intervened. Just as nature abhors a vacuum, Bernard abominates a mixed metaphor. 'Actually, Sir Humphrey,' he explained confidentially, 'you can't have a graveyard in a minefield because all the corpses would . . .' and he made a vague explosion gesture. Humphrey gave him a look which reduced him to silence.

I was more immediately interested in why Humphrey, who has been claiming that he got me this local government job, is now saying that it's a minefield and a graveyard. Was this a friendly act?

'Well, what *am* I supposed to do?' I asked.

'Um . . . yes, well . . . quite honestly Minister, I didn't think you'd *do* anything. I mean, you've never done anything before.'

I brushed aside the insult and the complaints. I told him I wanted specific proposals right away, and immediate plans for the implementation of failure standards by local authorities. I couldn't see why he was getting so worked up about it – and then, the penny dropped: these failure standards could be made to apply to Whitehall as well.

I'd just started to say something along those lines when Humphrey made a chance remark that immediately caught my attention.

'Minister, if you insist in interfering in local government, may I make a positive suggestion that could prove a very real vote-winner?'

I always try to make time to listen to a positive suggestion.

'There is an area of local government that needs urgent attention – Civil Defence.'

I thought at first that this was a completely frivolous suggestion. Everybody regards fall-out shelters as a joke.

He seemed to read my mind. 'At the moment, Minister, you may think they are a joke. But the highest duty of any government is to protect its citizens. And Local Authorities are dragging their feet.'

'Some people,' I said, 'think that building shelters makes nuclear war more likely.'

'If you have the weapons, you must have the shelters.'

'I suppose you're right. But I wonder if we really need the weapons.'

Sir Humphrey was shocked. 'Minister! You're not a unilateralist?'

I told him that I sometimes wonder. He told me that in that case I should resign from the government. I told him that I'm not *that* unilateralist.

'But after all, Humphrey,' I added, 'the Americans will always protect us from the Russians, won't they?'

'The Russians?' he asked. 'Who's talking about the Russians?'

'Well, the independent nuclear deterrent . . .'

He interrupted me. 'It's to protect us against the French.'

I could hardly believe my ears. The French? It sounded incredible. An extraordinary idea. I reminded Humphrey that they are our allies, our partners.

'They are *now*,' he agreed. 'But they've been our enemies for most of the past nine hundred years.'

It only needed a few seconds' thought to realise the profound truth of what he was saying. Suddenly it didn't seem at all incredible – just common sense, really. If the bomb is to protect us from the *French*, that's a completely different matter, obviously we've got to have it, you can't trust the Frogs, there's no room for discussion about *that*!

Furthermore, there is – unquestionably – increasing public concern about the bomb. And if one can be seen to be doing something about it, it could do one a lot of good politically.

Also I gathered at the Beeb that Ludovic Kennedy is preparing a TV documentary on Civil Defence, and it's bound to be critical of the current situation. So if I were seen to be taking decisive measures . . .

'When do we start?' I asked Humphrey.

He had an immediate suggestion. 'The London Borough of Thames Marsh has spent less on Civil Defence than any authority in the country.'

An excellent starting plan. Thames Marsh is Ben Stanley's borough, that odious troglodite with the wispy moustache. The press hate him.

So I told Bernard to set up the visit, and make sure the press are fully informed. 'Tell them,' I instructed him, 'that I lie awake at night worrying about the defenceless citizens of Thames Marsh.'

'Do you?' asked Bernard.

'I will now!' I said firmly.

July 8th

I made an official visit to Thames Marsh Town Hall today. There was a very satisfactory turn-out from the press, I noticed, especially photographers.

I met a so-called 'welcoming committee' on the front steps. Loads of flash-guns going off. I was introduced to the Leader of the Council.

'Mr Stanley, I presume,' I said. I'd prepared it of course, but it got a jolly good laugh from the assembled hacks.

The ensuing discussion over cups of tea and sticky buns in the Mayor's Parlour can hardly be described as a meeting of minds. But I made the point I had to make with great effectiveness, and I'm sure it will all be reported. If not, no doubt it will be leaked some-how. [*In other words, Hacker would leak it. – Ed.*]

Stanley opened the hostilities by asking me belligerently why I thought I could come swanning down to Thames Marsh from Whitehall, telling them how to run their borough.

In return, I asked him (politely) why he was doing less than any other borough in Britain to protect the people who elected him.

'Simple,' he said, 'we can't find the money.'

I suggested he try looking for it. This produced an outburst of anger, mixed with a good dose of self-satisfaction.

'Oh that's *great*,' he snapped, smiling a thin smile, strangely at variance with his malevolent, beady eyes, a crumb or two of the Mayor's Battenburg marzipan cake stuck to his twitching mous-tache. 'Oh that's great. Stop school meals? Buy no text books? Turn the OAPs[1] out into the cold?'

---

[1] Senior Citizens.

I wasn't impressed by all that cheap electioneering rubbish. It's nothing to do with our Senior Citizens.[1]

'If you want the money,' I said wearily, 'I can tell you exactly where you can find it.'

'You can?' he sneered.

'Yes,' I said. I told Cartwright to tell him, because he had the file. So Cartwright read him the list that he and I had approved.

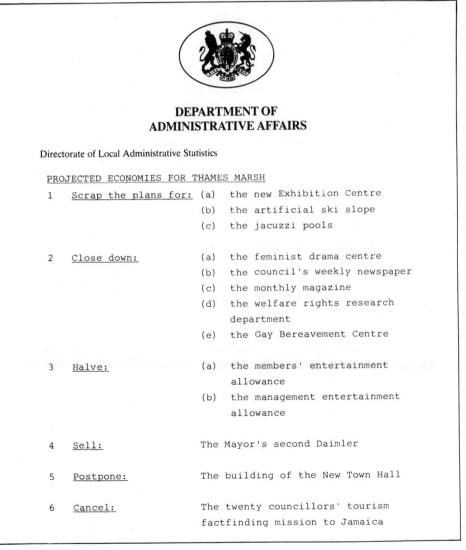

DEPARTMENT OF ADMINISTRATIVE AFFAIRS

Directorate of Local Administrative Statistics

PROJECTED ECONOMIES FOR THAMES MARSH

1	Scrap the plans for:	(a)	the new Exhibition Centre
		(b)	the artificial ski slope
		(c)	the jacuzzi pools
2	Close down:	(a)	the feminist drama centre
		(b)	the council's weekly newspaper
		(c)	the monthly magazine
		(d)	the welfare rights research department
		(e)	the Gay Bereavement Centre
3	Halve:	(a)	the members' entertainment allowance
		(b)	the management entertainment allowance
4	Sell:		The Mayor's second Daimler
5	Postpone:		The building of the New Town Hall
6	Cancel:		The twenty councillors' tourism factfinding mission to Jamaica

[1] OAPs.

This list of suggestions would save £21 million on capital account over five years, and £750,000 a year on revenue account.

Stanley read the list. There followed a bemused silence. Finally he came up with an answer.

'That's just stupid,' he said.

I asked why.

'Because,' he explained laboriously, 'it's depriving the disadvantaged of indispensable services.'

'Jacuzzi pools?' I asked innocently.

He knew only too well that he was on a very sticky wicket, so changed his line of defence.

'Look,' he said, completely abandoning the argument that Thames Marsh couldn't find the necessary money, 'I don't care whether we can afford fall-out shelters or not. This is a unilateralist borough. We don't believe in nuclear war in Thames Marsh.'

'Mr Stanley,' I replied carefully. 'I don't believe in nuclear war either. No sane man does. But the provision of fall-out shelters is government policy.'

'It is not Thames Marsh policy,' he snarled. 'Thames Marsh has no quarrel with the USSR.'

'It's not just the USSR we're scared of, it could be the Fr. . . .'

I stopped myself just in time. Had I completed that word I could have caused the biggest international incident of the decade.

'The who?' he asked.

I though fast. 'The fr . . . frigging Chinese' was all I could think of on the spur of the moment. But it served its purpose, and the crisis passed. And I kept talking. I thought I'd better. Not that it was difficult. The idea of each borough in the UK having its own foreign policy was too absurd to contemplate. The TUC has its own foreign policy, each trade union, now each borough, where is it going to end? Soon they'll all want their own Foreign Office – as if we haven't enough problems with the one we've got.

The irony is, in practice it is virtually impossible for *any* institution to have its own foreign policy, even the Government. The Foreign Office sees to that, with the help of Washington, NATO, the EEC and the Commonwealth Secretariat.

So I attempted to show him that he was suffering from delusions of grandeur.

'If the Russians ever invade us,' I suggested sarcastically, 'I suppose they'll stop at the borough boundaries, will they, and say: Hang on, we're not at war with the London Borough of Thames

Marsh. Right wheel Comrades. Annexe Chelsea instead?'

The discussion was becoming fairly heated. [*What the press state-ment would later describe as a 'frank exchange of views.' – Ed.*]

But at this moment Bernard intervened and, excusing himself from interrupting us, handed me a little note. It was most revealing. In no time at all I grasped its contents, and its political significance.

I looked at Comrade Ben. 'Oh Mr Stanley,' I said, trying not to smile, 'it seems that *you* would not be called upon to make the sup-reme sacrifice, in any case.'

'What do you mean?' he asked, knowing perfectly well what I meant.

The note contained the information that there is a fall-out shelter under Thames Marsh Town Hall, with a place reserved in it for, among others, the Leader of the Council. I asked if it was true.

'We didn't build it.' I'd got him on the defensive.

'But you maintain it?'

'It's only a very small one,' he muttered sullenly.

I asked him about his own place in it.

'I was persuaded with deep reluctance that my preservation was a necessity in the interests of the ratepayers of Thames Marsh.'

So I asked him what provision he had made for other essential people: doctors, nurses, ambulance men, firemen, civil rescue squads, emergency radio and television services? 'People who might be almost as important as councillors,' I added sarcastically.

'One of them's a chemist.'

'Oh great,' I said. 'Nothing like an aspirin for a nuclear holo-caust.'

[*Later that week Sir Humphrey Appleby lunched with Sir Arnold Robinson, the Cabinet Secretary, at the Atheneum Club. Sir Hum-phrey kept a memo of the meeting. – Ed.*]

Arnold observed that my Minister had enjoyed quite a little publicity triumph down at Thames Marsh. He seemed pleased, which surprised me.

I'm always worried when this Minister has a triumph of any sort. It invariably leads to trouble because he thinks he has achieved something.

Arnold thinks it's good when Ministers think they have achieved some-thing. He takes the view that it makes life much easier, because they stop fretting for a bit and we don't have to put up with their little temper tan-trums.

My worry, on the other hand, is that he will want to introduce his next idea.

Arnold was most interested to learn that we have a Minister with two ideas. He couldn't remember when we last had one of those.

[*Of course, Hacker had not really had any ideas. One was Bernard's and the other was Dr Cartwright's. – Ed.*]

Arnold wanted to know about the latest idea, and I was obliged to tell him that it was Cartwright's idiotic scheme to introduce pre-set failure standards for all council projects over £10,000, and to make a named official responsible.

Arnold knew about this scheme, of course, it's been around for years. But he thought (as I did) that Gordon Reid had squashed it. I think Arnold was a bit put out that Cartwright had got it to Hacker, though I don't see how I could have prevented it since Cartwright has now come over to the DAA. After all, he slipped it to the Minister privately, under plain cover. Brown envelope job.

Arnold was adamant that it must be stopped. He's absolutely right. Once you specify in advance what a project is supposed to achieve and whose job it is to see that it does, the entire system collapses. As he says, we would be into the whole squalid world of professional management.

Arnold reminded me (as if I didn't already know) that we already move our officials around ever two or three years, to stop this personal responsibility nonsense. If Cartwright's scheme goes through, we would have to be posting everybody once a fortnight.

Clearly we have to make the Minister understand that his new responsibilities are for enjoying, not for exercising.

I told Arnold that tomorrow Hacker will be living his little triumph all over again, recording a TV interview with Ludovic Kennedy for a documentary on Civil Defence.

Arnold wondered out loud what would happen if we gave Hacker a dossier of the curious ways in which local councillors spend their Civil Defence budgets. I remarked that I couldn't really see how that would help. But Arnold had an idea . . .

Perhaps he should become a Minister!

[*Appleby Papers 39/H1T/188*]

[*It was known that Hacker was delighted by the invitation, expected though it was, to appear on Ludovic Kennedy's television documentary on Civil Defence. He was under the impression that he was being given a chance to discuss a Ministerial success. Before the recording, in fact, it is said that he jocularly asked Kennedy if this represented a change of policy by the BBC.*

We reproduce the transcripts of the interview, which took a course that was, as it turned out, not to Hacker's liking. This, of course, was a result of Sir Arnold Robinson's idea. – Ed.]

BRITISH BROADCASTING CORPORATION

LUDOVIC: Minister, you've been claiming recently that you've been having some success in your dealings with local authorities on the matter of Civil Defence.

HACKER: Yes.

LUDOVIC: But hasn't this success been more in the field of publicity than any real achievement?

HACKER: No Ludo. I believe that local authorities are being made to face up to the need because of the increased public interest we are generating.

LUDOVIC: So you agree.

HACKER: What?

LUDOVIC: You are saying that your successes have only been publicity successes.

HACKER: Well, if you want to put it that way: yes. But things are changing.

LUDOVIC: In Thames Marsh?

HACKER: Ah. Thames Marsh. They do, as I have pointed out to the press, have one nuclear fall-out shelter. And one of its places is reserved for Mr Ben Stanley, the leader of the council, who is refusing to build shelters for others! Don't you think this is rather hypocritical?

LUDOVIC: But Minister, is it not reasonable for our elected representatives to be given a chance of survival? Otherwise, who will govern?

BBC tv

BRITISH BROADCASTING CORPORATION

HACKER: In the event of a nuclear holocaust there are more important people than mere politicians - doctors, nurses, firemen, all the people who run the essential services.

LUDOVIC: But don't the Prime Minister and the Home Secretary, for instance, have places reserved in a government fall-out shelter?

HACKER: Ah. Er, um, but ... um, but that's completely different.

LUDOVIC: Why?

HACKER: Well, someone has to er, run the ... you know.

LUDOVIC: But they're not trained in first aid and fire fighting, are they? Surely you're arguing that they should give up their places to doctors and nurses? Have you put it to them?

HACKER: I think we must be careful not to, er, trivialise a very important issue, Ludovic. To give another example, I have just been told of a borough that sent a council delegation to California at the ratepayers' expense to look at fall-out shelters. And when they got back they couldn't do anything about it because they'd spent their whole Civil Defence budget for three years on the trip.

LUDOVIC: Isn't that appalling?

HACKER: Appalling.

[*It is interesting to read Hacker's brief remarks in his diary, written on the evening of the television interview – Ed.*]

July 14th

TV interview went quite well. But I got into a bit of difficulty over Ben Stanley's bunker. I said that politicians weren't as important as doctors and so on.

He asked about the PM's place in a government shelter. I should have seen that one coming.

I got out of it, pretty cleverly on the whole. All the same I'm not sure how happy the PM will be about it.

Fortunately I was able to tell a marvellously funny story about a group of councillors who spent three years' Civil Defence budget on a jaunt to California. So that's all right. On the whole it should do me a bit of good when it goes out next week.

July 15th

A worrying day. I've put my foot in it with the PM in a much bigger way than I'd ever imagined.

That wretched story about the councillors going to California is the root of the trouble. I don't even remember where I got it from – it was in some brief that Bernard passed on to me from the Civil Defence Directorate before the TV programme, I think.

Anyway, Humphrey asked me about it. At first he wouldn't say why. He merely made the observation that he was sure that I knew what I was doing.

He only says that when I've made an appalling cock-up.

Then he revealed that the borough in question contains the PM's constituency. And the PM's election agent was the councillor who led the offending delegation.

At first I thought he was joking. But no.

'Number Ten have been trying to keep it quiet for weeks,' he said. 'Ah well. Truth will out.'

I couldn't see why. Truth mustn't out. That's the worst thing that can happen. It'll look like a personal attack, and the PM's very touchy about disloyalty at the moment. I told Humphrey that we must stop the interview going out. I could see no other alternative.

To my astonishment he chose that moment to get to his feet and bring the discussion to a close.

'Unfortunately Minister, I have no time. I must be going.'

I gasped. 'You can't. This is top priority. I order you.'

'Alas! Minister, it is your orders that are calling me away.'

I couldn't think what he meant. He explained: 'Your scheme for imposing pre-set failure standards on local councils is very complex. You asked for proposals straight away. It is taking every moment of my time. Much as I would like to help . . .'

He paused. Then he seemed to make a proposal. 'On the other hand, if implementing failure standards were not quite so urgent . . .'

'Do you mean,' I asked casually, 'you *could* stop the broadcast?'

He was guarded. 'Minister, we cannot censor the BBC. But . . . I happen to be having lunch tomorrow with the BBC's Director of Policy, perhaps you'd care to join us?'

I couldn't see any point, if we can't censor them. I said so, rather disconsolately.

But Sir Humphrey's reply has given me grounds for hope. 'No Minister, but we can always try to persuade them to withdraw programmes voluntarily once they realise that transmission is not in the public interest.'

'It's not in my interest,' I replied firmly, 'and I represent the public. So it can't be in the public interest.'

Humphrey looked intrigued. 'That's a novel idea,' he said. 'We've not tried that on them before.'

I think that he has more respect for my ideas than he likes to show.

July 16th

A very successful lunch today with Humphrey and Francis Aubrey, the BBC's Director of Policy, a man with a permanently anxious expression on his face. As well he might have.

It started badly though. As soon as I broached the subject he stated his position firmly. 'I'm sorry Mr Hacker, but the BBC cannot give in to Government pressure.' His black bushy eyebrows bristled sternly.

'Well let's leave that on one side, shall we?' said Sir Humphrey smoothly.

I thought Humphrey was supposed to be on my side.

'No really,' I began, 'I must insist. . .'

But he silenced me, rather rudely I thought. 'Let's leave that on one side,' he repeated. '*Please*, Minister.'

I had no option really. But I later realised that I had underestimated my Permanent Secretary.

He turned to Mr Aubrey and said: 'Frank, can I raise something else? There is considerable disquiet about the BBC's hostility to the Government.'

Aubrey laughed off the idea. 'That's absurd.'

'Well, *is* it?' asked Humphrey. And he leaned across to the empty chair beside him and opened up an enormous briefcase. Not his usual slimline leather job with gold engraved initials, but a big fat bulging leather bag, so heavy that his driver had carried it into the club for us.

I'd been preoccupied and worried, and I'd scarcely noticed it. If I had thought about it I suppose I'd have assumed it contained some documents with such a high security clearance that Humphrey had to take them with him everywhere he went.

In the event, it turned out that it contained a number of files that he intended to show the man from the Beeb.

'We have been documenting instances of bias in BBC current affairs.' He handed over a file with *Bias* written across it in a felt pen in large red letters. Francis Aubrey put down his knife and fork and was about to open it when Humphrey handed over a second file, with the words *Favourable News Stories Not Reported By The BBC*. Then he handed over one file after another, pointing out their contents.

Excessive Publicity For Other Countries' Case Against Britain – 'Especially our Common Market enemies. Er, partners, I mean,' explained Humphrey. *Jokes Against The Prime Minister. Unnecessary Publicity for Anti-government Demonstrations*. And finally, one huge file, much fatter than the others, which he heaved across the table, marked, *Ministers' Programme Suggestions Not Accepted*.

Francis Aubrey was clearly shaken by this mass of incriminating allegations and evidence. 'But . . . I'm . . . but I'm sure we've got answers to all these.' He sounded more firm than he looked.

'Of course the BBC's got answers,' I told him. 'It's always got answers. Silly ones, but it's always got them.'

Humphrey was taking a cooler line. 'Of course the BBC has explanations,' he said soothingly. 'But I just thought I ought to warn you that questions are being asked.'

'What sort of questions?' Mr Aubrey was looking even more worried.

'Well,' said Humphrey thoughtfully, 'for example, if Parliament were to be televised, whether it shouldn't be entrusted to ITV.'

'You can't be serious,' he exploded.

'And,' continued Humphrey in the same quiet and thoughtful vein, 'whether the BBC administration has really made the cuts in jobs and premises that we have endured in government. Should a Select Committee be appointed to scrutinise all BBC expenditure?'

Francis Aubrey started to panic. 'That would be an intolerable intrusion.' Resorting to pomposity to hide his thoroughly understandable fears.

I was enjoying myself thoroughly by this time.

'Of course,' said Sir Humphrey agreeably. 'And then there's the extraordinary matter of the boxes at Ascot, Wimbledon, Lords, Covent Garden, the Proms . . .'

I pricked up my ears. This was news to me.

Francis said, 'Ah yes, but these are a technical requirement. For production and engineering staff, you know.'

At this juncture Humphrey fished about at the bottom of his copious and now nearly empty Gladstone bag, and produced a box of photographs and press cuttings.

'Hmmm,' he said, and smiled and dropped his final bombshell. 'Reports suggest your production and engineering staff are all holding champagne glasses, all accompanied by their wives – or other ladies of equal distinction – and all bearing a remarkable similarity to governors, directors and executives of the corporation and their friends. I'm wondering whether it is my duty to pass the evidence to the Department of Inland Revenue. What's your view?'

And, with that, he handed over the box of photographs.

In silence, an ashen Francis Aubrey looked through them.

As he stopped at a splendid ten by eight portrait Humphrey leaned across, glanced at it, and observed, 'You've come out awfully well, haven't you?'

We fell into silence for some while. F.A. put down the photographs, tried to eat a little more of his Sole Meunière, but clearly it was turning to dust in his mouth. He gave up. I just watched with interest. Humphrey's performance was brilliant, and I had no wish to interrupt it or get in the way.

Humphrey was quietly enjoying his glass of Château Leoville-Barton 1973, a bottle of which he had carefully chosen to go with his roast beef. It tasted okay, though one glass of red is much like another as far as I'm concerned.

Finally Humphrey broke the silence. 'Mind you, I think we may just be able to contain all this criticism of the corporation, provided the files don't get any larger. That's why I am urging my Minister that there is no need to take up the case of the Civil Defence programme formally.'

Francis was looking desperate. He turned the photo of himself face downwards on the pile. 'Look, you do see my position. The BBC cannot give in to government pressure.'

'Of course not,' said Humphrey. This surprised me. I thought that that was precisely what we were trying to achieve. But I had reckoned without the hypocrisy of the Establishment. Or, to put it more kindly, Humphrey was devising some face-saving apparatus for Mr Aubrey.

And that's how it turned out to be. He looked at me.

'We wouldn't want the BBC to give in to government pressure. Would we Minister?'

'No?' I asked, slightly cautiously, recognising a clear cue.

'No of course we wouldn't,' he went on. 'But the Minister's interview with Ludovic Kennedy did contain some factual errors.'

Francis Aubrey seized on that. He brightened up considerably. 'Factual errors? Ah, that's different. I mean the BBC couldn't give in to government pressure . . ."

'Of course not,' we agreed.

'. . . but we set great store by factual accuracy.'

'Indeed,' said Humphrey, nodding sympathetically. 'And then, some of the information in the interview is likely to be out of date by the time of transmission.'

'Out of date?' he responded eagerly. 'Ah that's serious. As you know, the BBC couldn't give in to government pressure . . .'

'Of course not,' we agreed in unison.

'. . . but we don't want to transmit out of date material.'

I saw that I could help Humphrey now.

'And since the recording,' I interjected, 'I've discovered that I inadvertently let slip one or two remarks that might have security implications.'

'Such as?' he asked.

I hadn't expected that question. I thought he'd be too well-bred to ask.

Humphrey came to the rescue. 'He can't tell you what they are. Security.'

Francis Aubrey didn't seem to mind a bit. 'Ah well, we can't be too careful about security, I do agree. If the defence of the realm is at stake, we have to be very responsible. I mean, obviously the BBC can't give in to government pressure . . .'

'Of course not,' we chorused enthusiastically one more time.

'. . . but security, well, you can't be too careful, can you?'

'You can't be too careful,' I echoed.

'You can't be too careful,' murmured Humphrey.

'And in the end, it wasn't a very interesting interview anyway. All been said before. Bit of a yawn, actually.'

F.A. – or Sweet F.A. as I like to think of him now – had brightened up considerably by this time. Colour had returned to his cheeks. His eyes were no longer lustreless and dead. He was now able to expound on the matter of BBC policy and practice with renewed confidence.

'I mean,' he explained, 'if it's boring, and if there are inaccuracies and security worries, the BBC wouldn't *want* to put the interview out. That puts a completely different complexion on it.'

'Completely different,' I said happily.

'Transmission,' he went on, 'would not be in the public interest. But I do want to make one thing absolutely clear.'

'Yes?' enquired Humphrey politely.

'There can be absolutely no question,' Francis Aubrey stated firmly and categorically, 'of the BBC ever giving in to government pressure.'

I think it will be all right now.

July 17th

This afternoon Sir Humphrey popped in to see me. He had just received a message that the BBC had decided to drop my interview with Ludovic Kennedy. Apparently they feel it is the responsible course. Of course they do.

I thanked Humphrey, and offered him a sherry. As I thought about the events of the last few days a new thought occurred to me.

'You know,' I said, 'it seems to me that, somehow, I was trapped into saying those things that would embarrass the PM.'

'Surely not,' said Humphrey.

'Yes,' I said, 'I think I was dropped right in it.'

Humphrey derided this as a ridiculous thought, and asked how I could even think it. I asked him why it was ridiculous to think that Ludo tried to trap me.

'Who?' he asked.

'Ludo. Ludovic Kennedy.'

Humphrey suddenly changed his tune. 'Oh, *Ludovic Kennedy* tried to trap you. I see. Yes. I'm sure he did.'

We both agreed that everyone who works for the media is deceitful, and you can't trust them an inch. But, now I think about it, why was he so surprised that I was talking about Ludo? Who did he *think* I was talking about?

Still, he has got me out of a frightful hole. And it was quite clear what the *quid pro quo* was expected to be. I had to suggest that we lay off the local authorities.

'It must be admitted,' I was forced to concede, 'that local councillors – on the whole – are sensible, responsible people, and they're democratically elected. Central government has to be very careful before it starts telling them how to do their job.'

'And the failure standards?'

'I think they can manage without them, don't you think?'

'Yes Minister.'

And he smiled contentedly.

But I don't intend to let the matter drop for good. I shall return to it, after a decent interval. After all, we had a little unspoken agreement, an unwritten *détente* – but no one can hold you to an unspoken unwritten deal, can they?

3
The Moral Dimension

July 29th

I am writing this entry, not in my London flat or in my constituency house, but in the first-class compartment of a British Airways flight to the oil sheikdom of Qumran.

We have been en route to the Persian gulf for about four and a half hours, and we should be landing in about forty-five minutes.

I'm very excited. I've never flown first-class before, and it's quite different. They give you free Champagne all the way and a decent meal instead of the usual monosodium glutamate plus colouring.

Also, it's nice being a VIP – special lounge, on the plane last, general red carpet treatment.

We're going there to ratify the contract for one of the biggest export orders Britain has ever obtained in the Middle East.

But when I say 'we' I don't just mean me and Bernard and Humphrey. In fact, I asked for an assurance in advance that we couldn't be accused of wasting a lot of government money on the trip. Humphrey assured me that we were taking the smallest possible delegation. 'Pared to the bone' was the phrase he used, I distinctly remember. But now I realise that there may have been some ulterior motive in keeping me in the VIP lounge till the last possible minute.

When I actually got onto the plane I was aghast. It is *entirely* full of civil servants. In fact it transpires that the plane had to be specially chartered because there are so many of us going.

I immediately challenged Humphrey about the extravagance of chartering an aircraft. He looked at me as though I were mad, and said that it would be infinitely more expensive for all of us to go on a scheduled flight.

I'm perfectly sure that's true. My argument is with the size of the party. 'Who are all these people?' I asked.

'Our little delegation.'

'But you just said the delegation has been pared to the bone.'

He insisted that it was. I asked him, again, to tell me who they all are. And he told me. There's a small delegation from the FCO[1] because, although it's a DAA mission, the FCO doesn't like any of us to go abroad except under their supervision. I can't really understand that, foreign policy is not at issue on this trip, all we are doing is ratifying a contract that has already been fully negotiated between the Government of Qumran and British Electronic Systems Ltd.

Anyway, apart from the FCO delegation, there is one from the Department of Trade, and one from Industry. Also a small group from Energy, because we're going to an oil sheikdom. (If you ask me, that's completely irrelevant – I reckon the Department of Energy would still demand the right to send a delegation if we were going to Switzerland – they'd probably argue that chocolate gives you energy!) Then there's a Dep. Sec. leading a team from the Cabinet Office, a group from the COI.[2] And finally, the whole of the DAA mission: my press office, half my private office, liaison with other departments, secretaries, those from the legal department who did the contract, those who supervised the contract . . . the list is endless.

One thing's certain: it's certainly not been pared to the bone. I reminded Humphrey (who is sitting next to me but has nodded off after going at the free Champagne like a pig with his snout in the trough) that when we were going to meet the Qumranis in Middlesborough there were only going to be seven people coming with us.

'Yes Minister,' he had nodded understandingly. 'But Teeside is perhaps not quite so diplomatically significant as Qumran.'

'Teeside returns four MPs,' I remarked.

'Qumran controls Shell and BP.'

Then, suddenly, a most interesting question occurred to me.

'Why are *you* here?' I asked.

'Purely my sense of duty free,' is what I thought he had replied. I interrupted gleefully. 'Duty free?'

He held up his hand, asking to be allowed to finish what he was saying. 'Duty, free from any personal considerations.'

Then, changing the subject suspiciously quickly, he handed me a document headed *Final Communiqué*, and asked me to approve it.

[1] Foreign and Commonwealth Office.
[2] Central Office of Information.

I was still silently fuming about over a hundred Civil Service free loaders on this trip. The whole lot of them with their trip paid for, *and* getting paid for coming. Whereas when I'd asked if Annie could come too, I'd been told that a special dispensation would be needed from the King of Qumran before she could attend any public functions with me – and that, in any case, I'd have to pay for her fares, hotel bill, everything.

These bloody civil servants have got it all completely sewn up to their own advantage. This trip is costing me hundreds of pounds because Annie really wanted to come. She's sitting opposite, chatting to Bernard, looking as though she's having a thoroughly good time. That's nice, anyway.

Anyway, I digress. I suddenly realised what was in my hand. Humphrey had written a final communiqué *before* the meeting. I told him he couldn't possibly do that.

'On the contrary, Minister, you can't write the communiqué *after* the meeting. We have had to get agreement from half a dozen other departments, from the EEC Commission, from Washington, from the Qumrani Embassy – you can't do that in a few hours in the middle of the desert.'

So I glanced at it. Then I pointed out that it was useless, hypothetical, sheer guesswork – it may bear no relation to what we actually say.

Sir Humphrey smiled calmly. 'No communiqué ever bears any relation to what you actually say.'

'So why do we have one?'

'It's just a sort of exit visa. Gets you past the press corps.' Oh, I forgot to mention, the back third of this mighty aeroplane is stuffed with drunken hacks from Fleet Street, all on freebies too. Everyone except my wife, for whom I have to pay! 'The journalists need it,' Sir Humphrey was saying, 'to justify their huge expenses for a futile non-event.'

I wasn't sure that I liked my trade mission to Qumran being described as a futile non-event. He obviously saw my face fall, for he added: 'I mean, a great triumph for you. Which is why it's a futile non-event for the press.'

He's right about that. Journalists hate reporting successes. 'Yes, what they really want is for me to get drunk at the official reception.'

'Not much hope of that.'

I asked why not, and then realised I'd asked a rather self-incriminating question. But Humphrey seemed not to notice.

Instead, he replied gloomily, 'Qumran is dry.'

'Well, it is in the desert, isn't it?' I said and then I suddenly grasped what he meant. Islamic Law! Why hadn't I realised? Why hadn't I asked? Why hadn't he *told* me?

It seems that we can get a drink or two at our own Embassy. But the official reception and dinner are at the Palace. For five solid hours. *Five hours without a single drinkie.*

I asked Humphrey if we could manage with hip flasks.

He shook his head. 'Too risky. We have to grin and bear it.'

So I sat here and read the communiqué which was full of the usual guff about bonds between our two countries, common interests, frank and useful conversations and all that crap. Humphrey was reading the *FT*[1]. I was wondering what we would do if the talks were *so* far removed from what it says in the communiqué that we couldn't sign it. Suppose there were to be a diplomatic incident at the reception. I'd have to contact London somehow. I'd need some way of directly communicating with the Foreign Secretary, for instance, or even the PM.

And then the idea flashed into my mind.

'Humphrey,' I suggested tentatively, 'can't we set up a security communications room next door to the reception? At the Sheikh's Palace, I mean? With emergency telephones and Telex lines to Downing Street. Then we could fill it with cases of booze that we'll smuggle in from the Embassy. We could liven up our orange juice and nobody would ever know.'

He gazed at me in astonishment. 'Minister!'

I was about to apologise for going too far, when he went on, 'that is a stroke of genius.'

I thanked him modestly, and asked if we could really do it.

Musing on it for a moment, he said that a special communications room would only be justified if there were a major crisis.

I pointed out that five hours without a drink is a major crisis.

We decided that, as the pound is under pressure at the moment, a communications room could be justified.

Humphrey has promised his enthusiastic support for the project.

[*It seems that this diplomatically dangerous prank was put into effect immediately on arrival in Qumran. Certainly, British Embassy files show that instructions for installing a British diplomatic communications room were given on the day the Trade Mission arrived in*

---

[1] *Financial Times.*

Photo by courtesy of FCO, Middle East Desk

Qumran. Prince Mohammed gave his immediate permission and a telephone hot-line to Downing Street was swiftly installed, plus a scrambler, a couple of Telexes and so forth.

This temporary communications centre was situated in a small ante-room near to one of the Palace's main reception areas. The following day the British party arrived at the Palace. James Hacker was accompanied by his wife Annie. The Qumranis had found it difficult to refuse permission as Her Majesty the Queen had previously been received at the Palace and thus the precedent had been set for admitting special women on special occasions.

Shortly after the reception began, at which orange juice was being served, Hacker was presented with a gold and silver rosewater jar, as a token of the esteem in which the Qumrani government held the British. – Ed.]

August 1st

Yesterday we went to the teetotal reception at Prince Mohammed's palace, and today I've got the most frightful hangover.

Unfortunately I don't remember the end of the reception awfully clearly, though I do have a hazy memory of Sir Humphrey telling some Arab that I'd suddenly been taken ill and had to be rushed off to bed. Actually that was the truth, if not the whole truth.

It was a very large reception. The British delegation was a bloody sight too big to start with. And then there were an enormous number of Arabs there too.

The evening more or less started with the presentation to me of a splendid gift accompanied by diplomatic speeches about what a pleasure it is to commemorate this day. Subsequently, chatting with one of the Arab guests it transpired that apparently it's a magnificent example of seventeenth-century Islamic Art, or so he said.

I asked what it was for originally. He said it was a rosewater jar. I said I supposed that that meant it was for rosewater, and the conversation was already getting rather bogged down when Bernard arrived at my elbow with the first of the evening's urgent and imaginative messages. Though I must admit that, at first, I didn't quite follow what he was saying.

'Excuse me Minister, there is an urgent call for you in our communications room. A Mr Haig.'

I thought he meant General Haig. But no.

'I actually mean Mr Haig, Minister – you know, with the dimples.'

I nodded in a worried sort of way, said 'Ah yes' importantly, excused myself and hurried away to the communications room.

I must say Humphrey had seen to it that someone had set the whole thing up beautifully. Phones, Telex, a couple of our security chaps with walkie-talkies, cypher machines, the works.

And just in case the place was bugged by our hosts I was careful not to ask for a drink but to ask for the message from Mr Haig. Immediately one of our chaps poured some Scotch into my orange juice. It looked browner, but no one could really tell.

SIR BERNARD WOOLLEY RECALLS:[1]
The official reception at the Palace of Qumran was an evening that I shall never forget. Firstly, there was the extraordinary strain of covering up for Hacker's increasing drunkenness. And not only Hacker, in fact: several members of the British delegation were in on the secret and it was notice-

---

[1] In conversation with the Editors.

able that their glasses of orange juice became more and more golden brown as the evening wore on.

But that evening also saw the start of a most unfortunate chain of events that might have led to an early end of my career.

Mrs Hacker was the only woman present. They'd made her a sort of honorary man for the evening. And while Hacker was off getting one of his refills, she remarked that the rosewater jar would look awfully good on the corner table of her hall in London.

It fell to me to explain to her that it was a gift to the Minister.

At first she didn't understand, and said that it was his hall too. I had to explain that it was a gift to the Minister *qua* Minister, and that she would not be allowed to keep it. I was naturally mindful of the near-scandal caused by the Tony Crosland coffee pot incident, which had occurred only a few years earlier.

She wanted to know if they were supposed to give it back. Clearly not. I explained that it would have been a frightfully insulting thing to do. So she observed, rather sensibly, that if she couldn't keep it and couldn't give it back, she couldn't see what she *could* do.

I explained that official gifts become the property of the government, and are stored in some basement somewhere in Whitehall.

She couldn't see any sense in that. I couldn't either, except that clearly it is not in the public interest for Ministers to be allowed to receive valuable gifts from anybody. I explained that one might keep a gift valued up to approximately fifty pounds.

She asked me how you found out the value. I said that you get a valuation. And then she flattered me in a way that I found irresistible. She asked me to get a valuation, said that it would be 'wonderful' if it were less than fifty pounds, because it was 'awfully pretty', and then told me that I was absolutely wonderful and she didn't know what they would do without me.

Regrettably, I fell for it, and promised that I would see what I could do.

Meanwhile I was being sent on errands by Hacker. He returned from one of his many trips to the temporary Communications Centre which we'd set up, telling me loudly that there was a message for me from Mr John Walker. From the Scotch Office. Aware that we could easily be overheard, I asked if he meant the Scottish Office.

As I left very much in need of some whisky, Mrs Hacker asked if there was a message for her.

'Of course there is darling,' the Minister replied hospitably. 'Bernard will collect it for you if you give him your glass.' I shot him a meaningful look and he continued, 'if you give him your glass he'll get you some orange juice too.'

I stayed close to the Minister's side for most of the evening which was just as well because he continually made tactless remarks. At one point he was looking for Sir Humphrey and I led him across to where Sir Humphrey and a man named Ross (from the FCO) were talking to Prince Mohammed.

Unfortunately both Ross and Sir Humphrey looked like Qumranis when approached from behind, as they were both dressed in full Arab robes and

Prince Mohammed and Sir Humphrey Appleby – kindly lent by the Trustees of the Archives of the Anglo-Arabian Friendship League

headdresses. In spite of Prince Mohammed's presence, Hacker was unable to disguise his shock as Sir Humphrey turned. He asked Humphrey why on earth he was dressed up like that.

Sir Humphrey explained that this was a traditional Foreign Office courtesy to our hosts. Ross confirmed that this was spot on, and Prince Mohammed said that indeed he regarded it as a most warm and gracious compliment. Nonetheless Hacker took Sir Humphrey aside and, in a voice that had not been lowered sufficiently, said: 'I can't believe my eyes. What have you come as? Ali Baba?'

I really did find it most awfully funny. Old Humphrey began to explain that when in Rome . . . and so forth. Hacker wasn't having any truck with that.

'This is not Rome, Humphrey,' he said severely. 'You look ridiculous.' This was undeniably true, but Humphrey found it rather wounding to be told. Hacker didn't let it go at that, either. 'If you were in Fiji, would you wear a grass skirt?'

69

Humphrey replied pompously that the Foreign Office took the view that, as the Arab nations are very sensitive people, we should show them whose side we're on.

Hacker remarked: 'It may come as a surprise to the Foreign Office, but you are supposed to be on *our* side.'

I decided that their conversation should continue in private, so I interrupted them and told Sir Humphrey that the Soviet Embassy was on the line – a Mr Smirnoff. And then I told Hacker, who was looking distinctly thirsty, that there was a message for him from the British Embassy Compound. The school. A delegation of Teachers.

He brightened up immediately, and, hurrying off, made some dreadful pun about going to greet the Teachers at once, before the Bell's goes.

Prince Mohammed sidled up to me, and observed softly that we were all receiving a great many urgent messages. There was no twinkle in his eye, no hint that he had spotted that all the British orange juice was turning steadily browner – and yet, I wondered if he realised what was going on. To this day, of course, I still don't know.

Unwilling to prolong the conversation, I edged away. And I found myself face to face with a smiling Arab who had been close to me earlier in the evening when I was talking to Annie Hacker about the rosewater jar. This next conversation, with its fateful consequences, is the first reason why this whole evening is etched forever on my memory.

Although dressed in traditional Arab style, the smiling Arab spoke perfect English and clearly knew the West only too well.

'Excuse me, *Effendi*,' he began, 'but I could not help overhearing your conversation about valuing the gift. Perhaps I can help.'

I was surprised. And grateful. And I asked if he had any idea how much it was worth.

He smiled. 'Of course. An original seventeenth-century rosewater jar is very valuable.'

'Oh dear,' I said, thinking of Annie Hacker's disappointment.

'You are not pleased?' Naturally, he was a little surprised.

I hastened to explain. 'Yes – and no. I mean if it is too valuable, the Minister is not allowed to keep it. So I was hoping it wasn't.'

He understood immediately, and smiled even more. 'Ah yes. Well, as I was saying, an original seventeenth-century rosewater jar is very valuable but this copy, though excellently done, is not of the same order.'

'Oh good. How much?'

He was a very shrewd fellow. He eyed me for a moment, and then said, 'I should be interested to hear your guess.'

'A little under fifty pounds?' I asked hopefully.

'Brilliant,' he replied without hesitation. 'Quite a connoisseur!'

I asked him if he could sign a valuation certificate. He agreed, but added that our English customs are very strange. 'You are so strict about a little gift. And yet your electronics company pays our Finance Minister a million dollars for his co-operation in securing this contract. Is that not strange?'

Of course, I was utterly horrified. I said that I hoped he didn't mean what I thought he meant.

He smiled from ear to ear. 'Of course. I work for the Finance Ministry. I got my share of the money.'

'For what?'

'For keeping my mouth shut!'

It seemed to me that someone would be asking for that money back from him any time now. But excusing myself as quickly as I decently could, I made my way hurriedly through the crowd, looking for Sir Humphrey. Not easy as he was still dressed up like one of the natives.

I found Sir Humphrey talking to the Minister, of all people. Rather clumsily, I asked if I could have a word with Sir Humphrey in private. Hacker told me that I could speak freely. Momentarily nonplussed, because of the enormity of the information that I was about to reveal to Sir Humphrey, I came up with a foolproof way of removing Hacker from the room for a couple of minutes.

'Minister,' I said, 'you're wanted in the Communications Room. The VAT man.' He looked blank. 'About your '69 returns.' He must have had a great deal too much already for he just stared at me as if I was mad, until I was forced to say, 'Vat 69'.

'Ah. Ah. Yes,' he said, turned gleefully, bumped into a hovering prince, and spilt what was left of his previous drink.

'Bernard,' Sir Humphrey took me by the arm and led me quickly to one side. 'I'm beginning to think that the Minister's had almost as many urgent messages as he can take.'

I was glad he'd led me to a quiet corner. I immediately blurted out that I had just found out the most terrible thing: that the contract was obtained by bribery.

Sir Humphrey, to my intense surprise, was completely unconcerned. Not only that, he *knew*. He told me that all contracts in Qumran were obtained by bribery. 'Everybody knows that. It's perfectly all right as long as nobody knows.'

I was pretty sure that the Minister didn't know. I suggested telling him.

'Certainly not,' Sir Humphrey admonished me.

'But if everybody knows . . .'

'Everybody else,' he said firmly. 'You do not necessarily let Ministers know what everybody else knows.'

At the crucial moment in the discussion two people converged upon us. From our right, His Royal Highness, Prince Feisal. And from our left, the Minister, looking distinctly the worse for wear.

'Ah, Lawrence of Arabia,' cried Hacker as he lurched towards Sir Humphrey. 'There's a message for you in the communications room.'

'Oh?' said Sir Humphrey, 'who is it this time?'

'Napoleon,' announced the Minister, giggled, then fell to the floor.

[*Hacker's diary continues – Ed.*]

August 3rd

Back in England, and back at the office. Feel rather jet-lagged. I often wonder if we statesmen really are capable of making the wisest decisions for our countries in the immediate aftermath of foreign travel.

Today there was a most unfortunate story in the *Financial Times*, reporting a story from the French press.

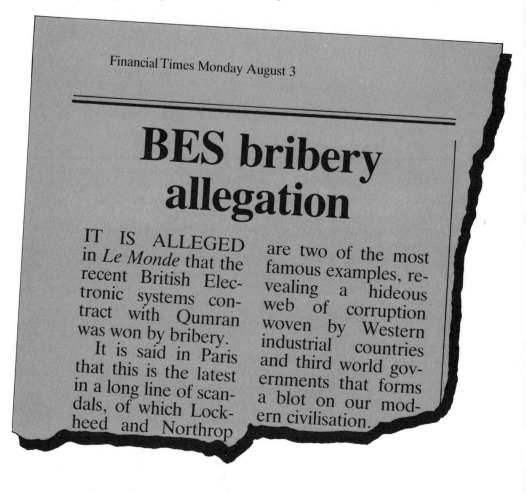

Financial Times Monday August 3

BES bribery allegation

IT IS ALLEGED in *Le Monde* that the recent British Electronic systems contract with Qumran was won by bribery.

It is said in Paris that this is the latest in a long line of scandals, of which Lockheed and Northrop are two of the most famous examples, revealing a hideous web of corruption woven by Western industrial countries and third world governments that forms a blot on our modern civilisation.

I showed it to Bernard. A lot of use that was!

'Webs don't form blots, Minister,' was his comment.

'What?' I said.

'Spiders don't have ink, you see. Only cuttlefish.' Sometimes I think that Bernard is completely off his head. Spiders don't have cuttlefish. I couldn't see what he meant at all. Sometimes I wonder if he says these idiotic things so that he can avoid answering my questions. [*Another sign of Hacker's growing awareness. – Ed.*]

So I asked him, directly, what he thought about publishing a baseless accusation of this kind against British Electronic Systems.

He muttered that it was terrible, and agreed with me that the squalid world of baksheesh and palm-greasing is completely foreign to our nature. 'After all, we *are* British,' I remarked.

He agreed without hesitation that we are British.

But there was something shifty in his manner. So I didn't let it drop. 'And yet,' I said, 'it's not like the *FT* to print this sort of thing unless there's something behind it.'

And I looked at him and waited. Bernard seemed to me to be affecting an air of studious unconcern.

'There isn't anything behind it, is there Bernard?'

He got to his feet, and looked at the newspaper. 'I think the sports news is behind it, Minister.'

Clearly there *is* something behind it, and clearly Bernard has been told to keep his mouth shut. Tomorrow I have a meeting with Humphrey first thing in the morning. And I intend to get to the bottom of this matter.

August 4th

My meeting with Humphrey.

I began by showing him the article in the *FT*. Though I think Bernard must have drawn his attention to it already.

I told him that I wanted to know the truth.

'I don't think you do, Minister.'

'Will you answer a direct question, Humphrey?'

He hesitated momentarily. 'Minister, I strongly advise you not to ask a direct question.'

'Why?'

'It might provoke a direct answer.'

'It never has yet.'

It was clear to me yesterday that Bernard knows something about all this. I don't think he was levelling with me. So today I put him on the spot, in front of Humphrey, so that he couldn't say one thing to his Minister and another to his Permanent Secretary. [*This brilliant move by Hacker struck at the heart of the entire Private Secretary system. – Ed.*]

'Bernard, on your word of honour, do you know anything about this?'

He stared at me like a frightened rabbit. His eyes flickered briefly at Sir Humphrey who – like me – was gazing at him in the hope (but

73

without the confidence) that he would say the appropriate thing.

Bernard clearly didn't know how to reply, proof enough that he knew something fishy had been going on.

'Well, I, er, that is, there was, er, someone did . . .'

Humphrey interrupted hastily. 'There was a lot of gossip, that's all. Rumour. Hearsay.'

I ignored Humphrey. 'Come on Bernard.'

'Um . . . well, one of the Qumranis did tell me he had received, er, been paid . . .'

'Hearsay, Minister,' cried Humphrey indignantly.

I indicated Bernard. 'Hearsay?'

'Yes,' Humphrey was emphatic. 'Bernard heard him say it.'

Clearly I was going to get nothing further out of Bernard. But he'd told me all I needed to know.

'Humphrey. Are you telling me that BES got the contract through bribery?'

He looked pained. 'I wish you wouldn't use words like "bribery", Minister.'

I asked if he'd prefer that I use words like slush fund, sweeteners, or brown envelopes. He patronisingly informed me that these are, in his view, extremely crude and unworthy expressions for what is no more than creative negotiation. 'It is the general practice,' he asserted.

I asked him if he realised just what he was saying. After all, I ratified this contract myself, in good faith. 'And in that communiqué I announced to the press a British success in a fair fight.'

'Yes,' he mused, 'I did wonder about that bit.'

'And now,' I fumed, 'you are telling me we got it by bribery?'

'No, Minister,' he replied firmly.

There seemed to be a light at the end of the tunnel. My spirits lifted. 'Ah,' I said, 'we *didn't* get it by bribery.'

'That's not what I said,' he said carefully.

'Well what *did* you say?'

'I said I am not telling you we got it by bribery.'

Pure sophistry if ever I heard any. It seemed there was no light at the end of the tunnel after all. Or if there was, it was turning out to be the proverbial oncoming train. So I asked him how he described the payments that had been made.

'You mean, how does the contract describe them?' he asked to make it clear that he would never describe them at all, under any circumstances.

To cut a long story short, Bernard gave me a list of informal guidelines for making these payments, a list that is in highly confidential circulation among top multi-national companies.

1 <u>Below £100,000</u>

        Retainers

        Personal donations

        Special discounts

        Miscellaneous outgoings

2 <u>£100,000 to £500,000</u>

        Managerial surcharge

        Operating costs

        Ex-gratia payments

        Agents' fees

        Political contributions

        Extra-contractual payments

3 <u>£500,000 +</u>

        Introduction fees

        Commission fees

        Managements' expenses

        Administrative overheads

        Advance against profit sharing

To me the scale of corruption was even more appalling than the fact that it was going on. [*A typical Hacker response. Clearly, corruption was perfectly acceptable to Hacker in smallish amounts. As subsequently became clear in the affair of the rosewater jar. – Ed.*]

I asked how the payments were generally made.

'Anything from a numbered account in the Swiss Bank to a fistful of used oncers slipped under the door of the gents.'

He was so casual about it. He couldn't see how shocking it was. He *said* he couldn't, anyway.

I spluttered almost incoherently about bribery and corruption being sin. And a criminal offence.

'Minister.' He gave me a patient smile. 'That is a narrow parochial view. In other parts of the world they see it quite differently.'

'Humphrey! Sin is not a branch of geography!'

But he argued that sin *is* a branch of geography, that in developing countries the size of the 'extra-contractual payment' is the means of showing how serious you are about the deal. When a multinational makes a big 'political contribution' it simply demonstrates that it expects big profits.

[*It is like a publisher's advance to an author. The one who pays the biggest advance is the one who is going for the biggest sales. – Ed.*]

'You're telling me,' I asked, 'that winking at corruption is government policy?'

'Oh no Minister! That would be unthinkable. It could never be government policy. Only government practice.'

His double standards leave me quite breathless.

In the middle of this unprecedented discussion [*Not so. – Ed.*] the press office rang. They wanted a statement about the Qumran bribery allegation. I had no idea what to say to them. I asked Humphrey for his help.

'I'm sure the press office can draft something convincing and meaningless,' he said obligingly. 'That's what they're paid for, after all.'

I told him he was an appalling cynic. He took that as a compliment, remarking that a cynic is only a term used by an idealist to describe realist.

I realised from his remark about the press office that he expected me to help with some cover-up if necessary. A shocking suggestion. Or implication, to be precise, since he hadn't exactly suggested it. And then, I also realised I had an alternative.

'I'll tell the truth,' I said abruptly.

'Minister! What are you thinking of!'

'I knew nothing of this. Why should I defend what I never approved?'

Then he trotted out all the usual stuff. That the contract is worth thousands of British jobs, and millions of export dollars, and that we can't throw all that away for some small technical irregularity.

I explained, again, that it is not a small technical irregularity, but corruption!

'No Minister, just a few uncontracted pre-payments . . .'

I had heard enough. I was forced to explain to him that government is not just a matter of fixing and manipulating. There is a moral dimension.

'Of course Minister. A moral dimension. I assure you it is never out of my thoughts.'

'So,' I went on, 'if this question comes up in the House, or if the papers start asking questions, I shall announce an inquiry.'

'Excellent idea,' he agreed. 'I shall be more than happy to conduct it.'

I took a deep breath. 'No Humphrey. Not an internal inquiry. A real inquiry.'

His eyes widened in horror. 'Minister! You can't be serious!'

'A real inquiry!' I repeated emphatically.

'No, no, I beg you!'

'The moral dimension.' It really is time moral issues were made central to our government once again. And I'm the man to do it.

SIR BERNARD WOOLLEY RECALLS:[1]

It was shortly after the day that Hacker threatened a real inquiry into the Qumran deal that I went to Hacker's London flat to collect him *en route* for an official visit to the Vehicle Licensing Centre in Swansea. Some morale-boosting was urgently called for down there, because the installation of the labour-saving computers had caused such delays that thousands more staff had been taken on to sort out the chaos. It looked as though larger computers would now be necessary, at some considerable public expense, partly in order to handle the situation and partly in order to avoid our having to lay off all the extra employees now working there. As job-creation was central to our strategy in the depressed or Special Development Areas [*i.e. Marginal Constituencies. – Ed.*] it was important to find something for these chaps to do. Clearly Hacker was not able to make any useful contribution in that area, but Sir Humphrey felt that a goodwill visit from the Minister would keep things friendlier for the time being and would make it look as though something was being done while we all racked our brains and tried to think what!

In any event, to cut a long story short [*Too late, – Ed.*] I was standing in the Minister's front hall chatting to Mrs Hacker, waiting for the Minister to finish dressing, when I saw the rosewater jar from Qumran, and commented that it looked awfully nice.

Mrs Hacker agreed enthusiastically, and added that a friend of hers had dropped in that day and had been frightfully interested.

'Really?'

[1] In conversation with the Editors.

'Yes.' And then she dropped the bombshell. 'Her name's Jenny Good-win–from *The Guardian*.'

'*The Guardian*,' I said, quietly stunned.

'Yes. She asked me where it came from.'

'A journalist,' I muttered, aghast.

'Yes. Well . . . *The Guardian*, anyway. She asked what it was worth, and I said about fifty quid.'

'You said about fifty quid.' My bowels had turned to water. I felt hot and cold simultaneously. I could hardly speak. I just tried to keep the conversation going somehow.

'Yes. Fifty quid.' She was looking at me strangely now. 'Funnily enough, she thought it was genuine.'

'She thought it was genuine,' I repeated.

'Yes, Bernard, you sound like an answering machine.'

I apologised.

Mrs Hacker then told me that the journalist, one Jenny Goodwin, had asked if she could ring up the Qumrani Embassy to ask what it was worth.

'To ask what it was worth,' I mumbled, hopelessly.

She looked at me keenly. 'It *is* only a copy, isn't it Bernard?' she asked.

I managed to say that so far as I knew, and so I was led to believe, and so forth, and then the Minister hurried downstairs and my bacon was saved. For the time being. But I knew that the jig was up and that my career was on the line, my neck was on the block, and my next appointment was likely to be at the Jobcentre in the Horseferry Road.

My only hope was that the Minister would come to my defence when the facts came out. After all, I'd always done my best for him. I didn't think I could expect much sympathy or help from Sir Humphrey. But I had no choice but to tell him the whole story as soon as I could.

[*The following morning Bernard Woolley made a special request for an urgent meeting with Sir Humphrey Appleby. Sir Humphrey made a note about it, which we found in the Departmental files at Walthamstow. – Ed.*]

BW requested an urgent meeting. He asked for a word with me. I said yes, and waited, but he did not speak. So I told him that I'd said yes.

Again he did not speak. I noticed that he was sweating, but it was a cool day. He seemed to be in a state of considerable mental anguish, such as I had never observed in him before.

I asked the standard questions. I thought perhaps that Woolley had sent the Minister to the wrong dinner, given him the wrong speech, or – worst of all – shown him some papers that we didn't mean him to see.

He shook his head silently, and I divined that the situation was even worse than that. So I told him to sit down, which he did gratefully. I waited.

It slowly emerged that the exquisite rosewater jar, given to the Minister in Qumran, was the root of the problem. Apparently the Minister's wife liked it. Not surprising. BW had explained the rules to her, and she had looked terribly sad. They always do. Then she had asked if it was really worth more than fifty pounds, and said how marvellous it would be if it wasn't. And BW, it seems, had agreed to 'help'.

I understand his motives, but a seventeenth-century vase – well, really!

BW then explained that there was a 'terribly nice Qumrani business man.' And this fellow had apparently valued it as a copy and not as an original. For £49.95. A most convenient sum.

I asked BW if he had believed this man. He wavered. 'I . . . er . . . he said he was an expert . . . well . . . he spoke Arabic awfully well, so I er . . . accepted his valuation. In good faith. After all, Islam is a jolly good faith.'

Not a convincing explanation, I felt. I told him that he had taken a grave risk, and he was fortunate that no one had asked any questions.

I was intending to let the matter drop, and merely record a reprimand in his report. But at this juncture he informed me that a journalist from *The Guardian* had seen the jar in Hacker's house, that Mrs Hacker had said it was a copy, and that further questions were to be asked.

It is a great tragedy that the press are so horribly suspicious about this sort of thing. But I told BW that we had no option but to inform the Minister.

[Hacker's diary continues – Ed.]
August 8th
Humphrey had made a submission yesterday (sounds like wrestling, doesn't it?) In other words, he submitted a paper to me, suggesting various methods of hushing up this bribery scandal.

Obviously I was not intending to go *out of my way* to reveal it. But equally I couldn't see how I could allow myself to be put in the position of sweeping bribery under the carpet. So if questions were asked, I had every intention of announcing a full independent enquiry chaired by a QC.

I explained this to Humphrey at the start of our meeting this morning. He started going on about the contract being worth £340 million. 'Get thee behind me Humphrey,' I said, and reminded him of the moral dimension of government. The contract may be worth £340 million, but my job's worth even more to me.

But then Humphrey told me that Bernard had something to tell me.

I waited. Bernard was looking very anxious. Finally he coughed and began to speak, rather haltingly.

'Um . . . you know that jar the Qumranis gave you?'

I remembered it well. 'Yes, we've got it in the flat. Most attractive.'

I waited. Clearly he was worried about something.

'I told Mrs Hacker that it was all right to keep it,' he said, 'because I had it valued at under fifty pounds. But I'm not sure . . . the man who valued it was awfully nice . . . I told him Mrs Hacker liked it a lot . . . but he might have been er, being helpful.'

I still couldn't see any problem. So I told him not to worry, and that no one will ever know. In fact, I was rash enough to congratulate him for being jolly enterprising.

Then came the bad news. 'Yes, but you see, Mrs Hacker told me this morning that a *Guardian* journalist came round and started asking questions.'

This was horrifying! I asked to see the valuation. It was written on the back of the menu. [*The Treasury were never awfully happy about valuations written on the backs of menus. – Ed.*]

I asked what the jar was really worth. Humphrey had the information at his fingertips. If it's a copy, then the valuation is roughly correct. But if it's an original – £5,000.

And I had kept it!

If I'd had a day or two to consider the matter there would have been no problem. It would have been pretty easy to dream up some valid explanation of the situation, one that got both me and Bernard off the hook.

But at that moment Bill Pritchard came bursting in from the press office. And he brought even worse news!

The Guardian had been on the phone to him. They'd been on to the Qumrani Embassy, telling them that my wife had said that this extremely valuable seventeenth-century thing presented to me by the Qumrani Embassy was a copy. The Qumrani Government was incensed at the suggestion that they insulted Britain by giving me a worthless gift. (Though I can't see the point of giving me a valuable gift if it's got to be stored in the vault forever.) The FCO then phoned Bill and told him it was building up into the biggest diplomatic incident since *Death of a Princess*.

I thought I'd heard enough bad news for one day. But no. He added that Jenny Goodwin of *The Guardian* was in the private office, demanding to see me right away.

I thought Annie had always described Jenny Goodwin as a friend of hers. Some friend! You just can't trust the media! Despicable, muck-raking nosey-parkers, always snooping around trying to get at the truth!

Bernard looked beseechingly at me. But it was clear that I had no choice.

'My duty is clear,' I said in my Churchillian voice. 'I have no choice.'

'No choice?' squeaked Bernard, like Piglet confronting the Heffalump.

I made it clear that indeed I had no choice. My wife had not asked him to lie about the value of the gift. He admitted she hadn't. I explained to Bernard that I fully realised that he had done this with the best of possible motives, but that there could be no excuse for falsifying a document.

He protested that he hadn't. But of course he was hair-splitting.

But my trouble is, I never know when to stop. I then launched into a tremendously self-righteous tirade. I told him that I cannot have it thought that I asked him to do this. Then I turned on Humphrey, and told him that I cannot have it thought that I will tolerate bribery and corruption in our business dealings. 'Enough is enough,' I went on, digging my own grave relentlessly. 'If this journalist asks me straight questions about either of these matters I must give straight answers. There is a moral dimension.'

I should have realised, since Humphrey was looking so thoroughly unflappable, that he had an ace up his sleeve. I didn't guess. And he played it.

'I agree with you Minister. I see now that there is a moral dimension to everything. Will I tell the press about the communications room or will you?'

Blackmail. Shocking, but true! He was clearly saying that if I laid the blame for (a) the bribery and corruption, or (b) the rosewater jar – *neither* of which were my fault – at his door or Bernard's door or *anyone's* door (if it comes to that) then he would drop me right in it.

I think I just gaped at him. Anyway, after a pause he murmured something about the moral dimension. Hypocritical bastard.

I tried to explain that the communications room was not the same thing at all. Completely different, in fact. Drinking is nothing to do with corruption.

But Humphrey would have none of it. 'Minister, we deceived the Qumranis. I am wracked with guilt, tormented by the knowledge that we violated their solemn and sacred Islamic laws in their own country. Sooner or later we must own up and admit that it was all your idea.'

'It wasn't,' I said desperately.

'It was,' they chorused.

I would have denied it, but it was their word against mine. And who would ever take the word of a mere politician against that of a Permanent Secretary and a Private Secretary?

Sir Humphrey piled on the pressure. 'Is it fifty lashes or one hundred?' he asked Bernard, who seemed to be brightening up a little.

In what seemed like an interminable pause, I contemplated my options. The more I contemplated my options the more they disappeared, until I didn't seem to have any at all. Finally Bill said that I had to meet the journalist or she would write something terrible anyway.

I nodded weakly. Humphrey and Bernard hovered. I knew that only one possible course was open to me. Attack! Attack is always the best form of defence, especially when dealing with the press.

And after all, dealing with the press is my stock-in-trade. That is what I'm best at.

[*That is what Ministers had to be best at. At that time the Minister's main role was to be the chief public relations man for his Ministry.* – Ed.]

I sized up her in no time as she came into the office. Attractive voice, slightly untidy pulled-through-a-hedge-backwards sort of look, trousers, absolutely what you'd expect from *The Guardian* – a typical knee-jerk liberal.

As she came in a rough strategy formed in my mind. I was charming, but cool, and gave her the impression that I was fairly busy and didn't have too much time to spare. If you don't do that, if you let them think that you think they are important, it confirms their suspicions that they are on to something.

So I adopted a brisk tone like the family doctor. 'What seems to be the trouble?' I asked in my best bedside manner.

'Two things,' she said, 'both of them rather worrying to the public.'

How dare she speak for the public, who know nothing about any of it? And never will, if I can help it!

She started with the French allegation of BES corruption in getting the Qumrani contract.

'Absolute nonsense,' I said categorically. If in doubt, always issue an absolute denial. And if you're going to lie, then lie with one hundred per cent conviction.

'But they quoted reports of payments to officials,' she said.

I pretended to lose my rag. I fixed her with a piercing gaze. 'This is absolutely typical. A British company slogs its guts out to win orders and create jobs and earn dollars, and what do they get from the media? A smear campaign.'

'But if they won by bribery . . .'

I talked over her. 'There is no question of bribery – I have had an internal inquiry and all these so-called payments have been identified.'

'What as?' she asked, slightly on the retreat.

Humphrey saw his opportunity to help.

'Commission fees,' he said quickly. 'Administrative overheads.'

He'd given me time to think – 'Operating costs. Managerial surcharge,' I added.

Bernard chimed in too. 'Introduction expenses. Miscellaneous outgoings.'

I thundered on. 'We have looked into every brown envelope,' I found myself saying, but changed it to 'balance sheet' in the nick of time. 'And everything is in order.'

'I see,' she said. She really didn't have a leg to stand on. She had no proof at all. She had to believe me. And I'm sure she knew only too well the risk of incurring the wrath of a Minister of the Crown with false allegations and accusations.

[*We get the impression that Hacker, like many politicians, had the useful ability to believe that black was white merely because he was saying so. – Ed.*]

I told her that the allegations she was making were the symptoms of a very sick society for which the media must take their share of the blame. I demanded to know why she wanted to put thousands of British jobs at risk. She had no answer. [*Naturally, as she did not want to put thousands of British jobs at risk. – Ed.*] I told her that I would be calling on the Press Council to censure the press for a disgraceful breach of professional ethics in running the story.

'Indeed,' I continued, rather superbly I thought, 'the Council, and the House of Commons itself must surely be concerned about the standards that have applied in this shameful episode, and pressure will be brought to bear to ensure that this type of gutter press reporting is not repeated.'

She looked stunned. She was completely unprepared for my counter-attack, as I thought she would be.

Nervously she collected herself and asked her second question, with a great deal less confidence, I was pleased to see. 'This rosewater jar, apparently presented to you in Qumran?'

'Yes?' I snapped, belligerently.

'Well . . .' she panicked but continued, 'I saw it in your house actually.'

'Yes,' I replied, 'we're keeping it there temporarily.'

'Temporarily?'

'Oh yes,' I was doing my ingenuous routine now. 'It's very valuable, you see.'

'But Mrs Hacker said it was an imitation.'

I laughed. 'Burglars, you silly girl. Burglars! We didn't want gossip going around. Until we've got rid of it.'

Now she was completely confused. 'Got rid of it?'

'Of course. I'm presenting it to our local museum when we get back to the constituency on Saturday. Obviously I can't keep it. Government property, you know.' And then I came out with my master stroke. 'Now – what was your question?'

She had nothing else to say. She said it was nothing, it was all right, everything was fine. I charmingly thanked her for dropping in, and ushered her out.

Humphrey was full of admiration.

'Superb, Minister.'

And Bernard was full of gratitude.

'Thank you, Minister.'

I told them it was nothing. After all, we have to stick by our friends. Loyalty is a much under-rated quality. I told them so.

'Yes Minister,' they said, but somehow they didn't look all that grateful.

4
The Bed of Nails

[*In politics, August is known as the 'silly season'. This is a time when voters are away on holiday, and trivial issues are pushed in the forefront of the press in order to sell newspapers to holidaymakers. It is also the time when the House of Commons has risen for the summer recess and is thus an excellent time for the government to announce new or controversial measures about which the House of Commons cannot protest until they reconvene in October – by which time most political events that took place in August would be regarded as dead ducks by the media.*

It follows that August is also the time when Cabinet Ministers are most off their guard. Members of Parliament are not at hand to question them or harass them, and the Ministers themselves – secure from the unlikely event of an August reshuffle and secure from serious press coverage of their activities – relax more than they should.

Perhaps this is the explanation of the transport policy crisis, which very nearly led to Hacker taking on one of the most unpopular jobs in Whitehall. How he evaded it is a tribute to the shrewd guiding hand of Sir Humphrey, coupled with Hacker's own growing political skills.

Early in the month a meeting took place at Ten Downing Street between Sir Mark Spencer, the Prime Minister's Chief Special Advisor, and Sir Arnold Robinson, the secretary to the Cabinet. Sir Mark's files contain no reference to this meeting, but as he was not a career civil servant this is not surprising. But Sir Arnold Robinson's diary, recently found in the Civil Service archives Walthamstow, reveal a conspiracy in the making. – Ed.]

August 11th.

Lunched with Sir Mark Spencer today. He and the P.M. are keen to bring in an integrated transport policy. I suggested that Hacker could be the best man for the job, as he doesn't know anything at all about the subject. The Secretary of State for Transport, who knows a lot about it, won't touch it with a ten foot barge pole. M.S. and I agreed that this job was indeed a bed of nails, a crown of thorns, a booby trap – which is why I suggested Hacker, of course.

Lunched with Sir Mark Spencer today. He and the PM are keen to bring in an integrated transport policy.

I suggested that Hacker could be the best man for the job, as he doesn't know anything at all about the subject. The Secretary of State for Transport, who knows a lot about it, won't touch it with a ten foot barge pole. M.S. and I agreed that this job was indeed a bed of nails, a crown of thorns, a booby trap – which is why I suggested Hacker.

He is ideally qualified, as I explained to M.S., because the job needs a particular talent – lots of activity, but no actual achievement.

At first M.S. couldn't see how to swing it on Hacker. The answer was obvious: we had to make it seem like a special honour.

The big problem was to get Hacker to take it on before Humphrey Appleby hears of it, because there's no doubt that Old Humpy would instantly smell a rat. '*Timeo danaos et dona ferentes*'[1] he would be sure to say, though he'd probably have to say it in English for Hacker's benefit as Hacker went to the LSE[2].

It seemed clear that we had to get a commitment today, especially as my departure for the Florida Conference on 'Government and Participation' is both imminent and urgent, tomorrow at the latest. [*During the 1970s and 1980s it was the custom for senior government officials to send themselves off on futile conferences to agreeable resorts at public expense during the month of August. – Ed.*]

Hacker came to meet us at tea-time. I had resolved to flatter him, which almost invariably leads to success with politicians, M.S. and I agreed therefore that we would give the job the title of Transport Supremo, which was a lot more attractive than Transport Muggins.

[1] 'Beware of Greeks bearing gifts' is the usual rough translation.
[2] London School of Economics.

I was also careful not to inform him in advance of the purpose of the meeting, partly because I did not want him to have the opportunity to discuss it with Humpy, and partly because I knew he would be anxious about being summoned to Number Ten. This would surely make him more pliable.

Events turned out precisely as I anticipated. He knew nothing whatever about transport, floundered hopelessly, was flattered to be asked and accepted the job.

It is fortunate that I shall be leaving for the country tonight, before Humpy gets to hear about all this.

[*It is interesting to compare the above recollections with Hacker's account of the same day's events in his diary. – Ed.*]

August 11th

An absolutely splendid day today, with a big boost for my morale.

I was summoned to meet Mark Spencer at Number Ten. Naturally I was a bit wary, especially as I knew the PM hadn't been awfully pleased to hear about that business with the rosewater jar, even though no harm came of it all in the end. I thought I might be in for a bit of a wigging, for when I got there I was met by Arnold Robinson, the Cabinet Secretary.

However, the meeting was for quite a different purpose – I've been promoted.

Arnold kicked off by saying they wanted to offer me something that was rather an honour. For a split second I was horrified – I thought they were telling me I was to be kicked upstairs. It was a nasty moment. But, in fact, they want to put me in charge of a new integrated national transport policy.

They asked me for my views on transport. I had none, but I don't think they realised because I carefully invited them to explain themselves further. I'm sure they thought that I was merely playing my cards close to my chest.

'We've been discussing a national integrated transport policy,' they said.

'Well, why not?' I replied casually.

'You're in favour?' enquired Sir Arnold quickly.

I thought the answer required was 'yes' but I wasn't yet sure so I contented myself by looking enigmatic. I'm sure that they were by now convinced that I was sound, because Sir Mark continued: 'Unfortunately, public dissatisfaction with the nationalised transport industries is now at a high enough level to worry the government, as you know.'

Again he waited. 'Can you go on?' I enquired.

He went on. 'We need a policy.' I nodded sagely. 'It's no good just blaming the management when there's a R in the month and blaming the unions the rest of the time.'

Sir Arnold chipped in. 'And unfortunately now they've all got together. They all say that it's all the government's fault – everything that goes wrong is the result of not having a national transport policy.'

This was all news to me. I thought we had a policy. As a matter of fact, I specifically recall that in our discussions prior to the writing of our manifesto we decided that our policy was not to have a policy. I said so.

Sir Mark nodded. 'Be that as it may,' he grunted, 'the PM now wants a *positive* policy.'

I wished Sir Mark had said so earlier. But I can take a hint, and it was not too late. 'Ah, the PM, I see.' I nodded again. 'Well. I couldn't agree more, I've always thought so myself.'

Sir Arnold and Sir Mark looked pleased, but I still couldn't see what it had to do with me. I assumed that it was a Department of Transport matter. Sir Arnold disabused me.

'Obviously the Transport Secretary would love to get his teeth into the job, but he's a bit too close to it all.'

'Can't see the wood for the trees,' said Sir Mark.

'Needs an open mind. Uncluttered,' added Sir Arnold.

'So,' said Sir Mark, 'the PM has decided to appoint a Supremo to develop and implement a national transport policy.'

A *Supremo*. I asked if I were the PM's choice. The knights nodded. I must admit I felt excited and proud and really rather overwhelmed by this extraordinary good piece of news. And there were more compliments to come.

'It was decided,' said Sir Mark, 'that you had the most open mind of all.'

'And the most uncluttered,' added Sir Arnold. They really were grovelling.

I naturally responded cautiously. Firstly because I simply couldn't imagine what the job entailed, and secondly it's always good to play hard to get when you're in demand. So I thanked them for the honour, agreed that it was a pretty vital and responsible job, and asked what it entailed.

'It's to help the consumer,' said Sir Mark. Though when Sir Arnold laboriously pointed out that helping the consumer was always a vote-winner, I reminded him firmly that I was interested purely because I saw it as my duty to help. My sense of public duty.

During the conversation it gradually became clear what they had in mind. All kinds of idiocies have occurred in the past, due to a lack of a natural integrated policy. Roughly summarising now, Sir Mark and Sir Arnold were concerned about:

1 *Motorway planning:* Our motorways were planned without reference to railways, so that now there are great stretches of motorway running alongside already existing railways.

   As a result, some parts of the country are not properly served at all.

2 *The through-ticket problem:* If, for instance, you want to commute from Henley to the City, you have to buy a British Rail ticket to Paddington and then buy an underground ticket to the Bank.

3 *Timetables:* The complete absence of combined bus and railway timetables.

4 *Airport Links:* Very few. For instance, there's a British Rail Western Region line that runs less than a mile north of Heathrow – but no link line.

5 *Connections:* Bus and train services don't connect up, all over London.

Sir A and Sir M outlined these problems briefly. They added that there are probably problems outside London too, although understandably they didn't know about them.

The possibilities are obviously great, and it's all very exciting. I suggested having a word with Humphrey before I accepted responsibility, but they made it plain that they wanted *my* opinion and approval. Not his. Rather flattering, really. Also, it shows that they have finally realised that I'm not a straw man – I really run my Department, not like *some* Ministers.

Furthermore it transpired that the PM was due to leave for the Airport in thirty minutes on the long trip involving the Ottawa Conference, and the opening of the UN General Assembly in New York, and then on to the meeting in Washington.

Jokingly I asked, 'Who's going to run the country for the next week?' but Sir Arnold didn't seem awfully amused.

Sir Mark asked if he could give the PM the good news that I had taken on the job on the way to the Airport.

Graciously, I agreed.

Hacker leaving Downing Street after the meeting (London Press Association)

August 12th

At an early morning meeting with Sir Humphrey, I told him I had good news. 'I've got a new job,' I began.

'Oh dear, the Department will be awfully sorry to lose you,' he responded pleasantly. A bit *too* pleasantly, perhaps.

But I explained that it was merely an extra job, developing and implementing an integrated national transport policy. At the special request of the PM. My Permanent Secretary did not seem pleased. In fact, he seemed to flinch.

'I see,' he replied. 'And what was the *good* news?'

I thought he must have misheard, so I told him again.

'So how,' he enquired drily, '*if* I may be so bold as to enquire, would you define *bad* news?'

I asked him to explain himself.

'Minister,' he said with a heavy sigh, 'are you aware what this job would mean if you accepted it?'

'I have accepted it.'

His mouth dropped open. 'You've *what*?' he gasped.

'I have accepted it.' I went on to explain that it is an honour, and also that we need a transport policy.

'If by "we" you mean Britain, that's perfectly true,' he acknowledged. 'But if by "we" you mean you and me and this Department, we need a transport policy like an aperture in the cranial cavity.'[1]

He went on to describe the job as a bed of nails, a crown of thorns, and a booby trap.

At first I thought he was just being silly or lazy or something. I could see that it would cause him some extra administrative problems, but on the other hand, it usually gave Humphrey pleasure to add to his empire – bigger budget, more staff, all that sort of thing.

'No Minister, the point is, that *you* are the one who is at risk. My job, as always, is merely to protect the seat of your trousers. The reason that there has never been an integrated transport policy is that such a policy is in everybody's interest *except* the Minister who creates it.'

I couldn't see why.

Humphrey paused for a minute, and gazed at the ceiling contemplatively. 'How can I put it in a manner that is close to your heart?' he asked himself. I waited. So did Bernard. 'Ah, I have it,' he murmured, turning to look at me straight in the eye. 'It is the ultimate vote-loser.'

I was stunned. Vote-*loser*?

Sir Humphrey explained, 'Why do you think the Transport Secretary isn't doing this?'

I was just about to reply that the Transport Secretary is apparently too close to it and can't see the wood for the trees, when Sir Humphrey said: 'He's too close to it, I suppose? Can't see the wood for the trees? Is that what they told you?'

'You tell me another reason then,' I challenged him.

'Why do you think the Transport Secretary suggested the Lord Privy Seal? Why do you think the Lord Privy Seal suggested the Chancellor of the Duchy of Lancaster? Why do you think *he* suggested the Lord President of the Council?'

I had to confess I knew nothing of all this.

Sir Humphrey continued relentlessly. 'And why do you think they invited you to Number Ten behind my back?' I must admit that this explanation never occurred to me. 'Minister, this hideous appointment has been hurtling round Whitehall for the last three weeks like a grenade with the pin taken out.'

He may be right, of course. He's usually pretty well up on all the

---

[1] A hole in the head.

gossip. But I was not about to concede the point. I felt that Humphrey's attitude was coloured by sour grapes – sour grapes that I had been honoured in this way, and sour grapes that he hadn't been consulted, either by them or by me.

'If I can pull it off,' I said carefully, 'it will be a feather in my cap.'

'If you pull it off,' said Bernard, 'it won't be in your cap any more.' I scowled at him, and he went pink and studied his shoes.

Sir Humphrey wasn't impressed with my argument. He believes that if I do pull it off, no one will feel the benefits for ten years, and long before that we will both have moved on. Or up. Or out.

'In the meantime,' he continued, 'formulating policy means making choices. Once you make a choice you please the people you favour but you infuriate everyone else. This is liable to end up as one vote gained, ten lost. If you give a job to the road services, the Rail Board and unions will scream. If you give it to the railways, the road lobby will massacre you. If you cut British Airways' investment plans they'll hold a devastating press conference the same afternoon. And you can't expand, because an overall saving is the Treasury's fundamental requirement.'

I voiced the small hope that, as I am to be the Transport Supremo, my views might carry some weight.

Humphrey could not disguise the sneer on his face. 'Transport Muggins is the Civil Service vernacular, I'm afraid. All the enemies you will make are experts in manipulating the media. PROs, Trades Unionists, MPs in affected constituencies. There'll be someone on television every night vilifying Hacker's Law, saying that you are a national disaster.'

His attitude angered me. I reminded him that the PM has asked me to perform this task, this necessary duty for my country. I always do my duty. Furthermore, Sir Mark believes that there are votes in it, and, if so, I certainly do not intend to look a gift horse in the mouth.

'I put it to you,' replied Sir Humphrey, 'that you are looking a *Trojan* Horse in the mouth.'

I wasn't quite sure what he meant by this. 'Do you mean,' I asked, 'that if we look closely at this gift horse we'll find it's full of Trojans?'

Bernard tried to interrupt, but I silenced him with a look. Sir Humphrey insisted that he be given a chance to prove his point, and offered to arrange a meeting, a preliminary discussion, with Under-Secretaries from the Department of Transport – the Road Division, the Rail Division and the Air Transport Division. 'I think it may illustrate the extent of some of the problems you will encounter.'

'You can arrange it if you like,' I told him. 'But I intend to take this on. If I succeed this could be my Falkland Islands.'

'Yes,' agreed Sir Humphrey, 'and you could be General Galtieri.'

August 13th

When I arrived in my office today I found the most curious memo from Bernard sitting on my desk.

Memorandum

From: *The Private Secretary*

To: *The Minister*

Aug 12th

CONFIDENTIAL, FOR THE MINISTER'S EYES ONLY

With reference to your comment at yesterday's meeting with the Permanent Secretary at which you enquired, in connection with looking the Integrated Transport Policy gift horse in the mouth, whether, if the gift horse were a Trojan Horse (as suggested by the Permanent Secretary that so it might prove to be) it would be full of Trojans.

Aug. 12th

CONFIDENTIAL, FOR THE MINISTER'S EYES ONLY.

With reference to your comment at yesterday's meeting with the Permanent Secretary, at which you enquired, in connection with looking the Integrated Transport Policy gift horse in the mouth, whether, if the gift horse were a Trojan Horse (as suggested by the Permanent Secretary that so it might prove to be) it would be full of Trojans.

May I respectfully draw the Minister's attention to the fact that, if he had looked the Trojan Horse in the mouth, he would have found Greeks inside.

The reason, of course, is that it was the Greeks who gave the Trojan Horse to the Trojans. Therefore, technically it was not a Trojan Horse at all. In fact, it was a Greek Horse. Hence the tag 'Timeo danaos et dona ferentes', which, as the Minister will recall, is usually and somewhat inaccurately translated as Beware of Greeks Bearing Gifts, or doubtless the Minister would recall had he not attended the LSE.

B.W.

I dictated a reply to Bernard, in which I said that Greek tags are all very interesting in their way, especially to classicists no doubt, but that they were not exactly central to government business.

I added that presumably the modern EEC version of that tag would be Beware of Greeks Bearing An Olive Oil Surplus.

(Rather good that. I must remember to use it next time I have to make an anti-EEC speech.)

To my astonishment, I found yet another memo from Bernard in my red boxes tonight, shortly before writing this entry in my diary. He really is tireless in his pursuit of pointless pedantry.

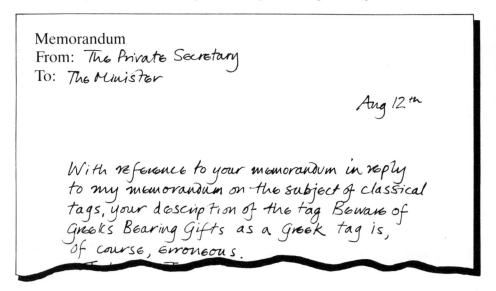

Memorandum
From: The Private Secretary
To: The Minister

Aug 12th

With reference to your memorandum in reply to my memorandum on the subject of classical tags, your description of the tag Beware of Greeks Bearing Gifts as a Greek tag is, of course, erroneous.

Aug. 12th

With reference to your memorandum in reply to my memorandum on the subject of classical tags, your description of the tag Beware of Greeks Bearing Gifts as a Greek tag is, of course, erroneous.

Just as the Trojan Horse was Greek, the tag which you described as Greek was, in fact, Latin. In fact, this is obvious if you consider that the Greeks would hardly suggest bewaring of themselves – if one can use such a participle: bewaring, that is – and the tag can clearly be seen to be Latin rather than Greek not because 'timeo' ends in 'o' (because the Greek first person also ends in 'o') – actually, if I may digress, there is a Greek word 'timao' meaning 'I honour' – but because the 'os' ending is a nominative singular termination of the second declension in Greek and an accusative plural in Latin.

Incidentally, as a fine point of interest, Danaos is not only the Greek for Greek but also the Latin for Greek.

B.W.

I shall preserve Bernard's memos for posterity. They give a clear indication of how academic brilliance can mislead those who recruit administrative trainees into the Civil Service.

[*A few days later Hacker, Appleby and Bernard Woolley were present at the promised meeting with three Department of Transport Under-Secretaries. – Ed.*]

August 17th

We have had a most extraordinary meeting today, the one that Humphrey had promised to arrange with the Under-Secretaries from the Department of Transport.

I can't remember all their names, but each one was from a different division – one from Air, one from Road and one from Rail. It was extraordinarily acrimonious. The one thing that they were all agreed on was that, somehow, my proposals were deeply misguided.

The man from Road Transport, Graham something or other, suggested that it should be government policy to designate road haulage as its own principle means of freight transport. He was promptly interrupted by Richard somebody with a rather irritable thin tired-looking creased face – not surprising when you consider he's been trying to modernise the railways and battle with BR, the NUR and ASLEF for most of his career.

'With the greatest possible respect, Minister, I think that such a policy would be, not to put too fine a point on it, unacceptably short-sighted. It is rail transport that must surely be the favoured carrier under any sane national policy.'

Piers, a smooth fellow from Air, interrupted so fast that he scarcely gave himself time to utter his usual courteous but meaningless preamble. 'If-I-might-crave-your-indulgence-for-a-moment-Minister, I have to say that *both* those proposals are formulae for disaster. Long-term considerations absolutely mandate the expansion of air freight to meet rising demand.'

Graham (Roads) put down his pencil, with a sharp click as it hit my mahogany reproduction conference table. 'Of course,' he snapped, 'if the Minister is prepared for a massive budget increase . . .'

'If the Minister will accept a long and unbelievably bitter rail strike . . .' interrupted Richard.

And Piers butted in: 'If the public can tolerate a massive rise in public discontent . . .'

I interrupted *them* by holding up my hand. They then confined themselves to staring at each other with intense mutual hostility.

95

'Hold on, hold on,' I said. 'We're the government, aren't we?'

'Indeed you are, Minister,' Sir Humphrey corrected me.

'So,' I continued, searching for agreement, 'we're all on the same side, aren't we?'

'Indeed we are/quite so/absolutely no question,' replied Richard, Piers and Graham roughly in concert.

'And,' I went on patiently, 'we are trying to find out what's best for Britain.'

Piers put up his hand. I nodded at him. 'Through the chair,' he said, 'I hardly think the end of the national air freight business is best for Britain?'

Our truce had lasted a mere twenty seconds. The war was on again. 'I find it hard to see how Britain is saved by the destruction of the railways,' Richard remarked bitterly.

And Graham, not to be outdone, added with heavy sarcasm that it was not immediately apparent to him how Britain would benefit from a rapid deterioration of the road network.

Again I took a lead. I explained that I was merely trying to examine a few policy options for the government's own freight transport needs. And that therefore I had thought that a preliminary chat with a few friends, advisors, around the table, could lead to some *positive, constructive* suggestions.

I should not have wasted my breath. The positive constructive suggestions were somewhat predictable. Richard promptly suggested a firm commitment to rail transport, Graham a significant investment in motorway construction, and Piers a meaningful expansion of air freight capacity!

So at this point I explained that my overall brief is, among other things, to achieve an overall cut in expenditure.

'In that case,' said Richard grimly, 'there is only one possible course.'

'Indeed there is,' snapped Graham.

'And there can be no doubt what it is,' Piers added in an icy tone.

They all eyed each other, and me. I was stuck. Sir Humphrey came to the rescue.

'Good,' he said with a cheerful smile, 'I always like to end a meeting on a note of agreement. Thank you gentlemen.'

And they filed out.

The meeting is the sort that would be described in a communiqué as 'frank'. Or even 'frank, bordering on direct', which means that the cleaners have to mop up the blood in the morning.

SIR BERNARD WOOLLEY RECALLS:[1]

The Minister found his meeting with the three Under-Secretaries confusing. This was because of his failure to understand the role of the Civil Service in making policy.

The three Under-Secretaries whom we met that morning were, in effect, counsel briefed by the various transport interests to resist any aspects of government policy that might have been unfavourable to their clients.

This is how the Civil Service in the 1980s actually worked in practice. In fact, all government departments – which in theory collectively represented the government to the outside world – in fact lobbied the government on behalf of their own client pressure group. In other words, each Department of State was actually controlled by the people whom it was supposed to be controlling.

Why – for instance – had we got comprehensive education throughout the UK? Who wanted it? The pupils? The parents? Not particularly.

The actual pressure came from the National Union of Teachers, who were the chief client of the DES.[2] So the DES went comprehensive.

Every Department acted for the powerful sectional interest with whom it had a permanent relationship. The Department of Employment lobbied for the TUC, whereas the Department of Industry lobbied for the employers. It was actually rather a nice balance: Energy lobbied for the oil companies, Defence lobbied for the armed forces, the Home Office for the police, and so on.

In effect, the system was designed to prevent the Cabinet from carrying out its policy. Well, somebody had to.

Thus a national transport policy meant fighting the *whole* of the Civil Service, as well as the other vested interests.

If I may just digress for a moment or two, this system of 'checks and balances', as the Americans would call it, makes nonsense of the oft-repeated criticism that the Civil Service was right wing. Or left wing. Or any other wing. The Department of Defence, whose clients were military, was – as you would expect – right wing. The DHSS, on the other hand, whose clients were the needy, the underprivileged and the social workers, was (predictably) left wing. Industry, looking after the Employers, was right wing – and Employment (looking after the *un*employed, of course) was left wing. The Home Office was right wing, as its clients were the Police, the Prison Service and the Immigration chaps. And Education, as I've already remarked, was left wing.

You may ask: What were we at the DAA? In fact, we were neither right nor left. Our main client was the Civil Service itself, and therefore our real interest was in defending the Civil Service against the Government.

Strict constitutional theory holds that the Civil Service should be committed to carrying out the Government's wishes. And so it was, as long as the Government's wishes were practicable. By which we meant, as long as *we* thought they were practicable. After all, how else can you judge?

---

[1] In conversation with the Editors.
[2] Department of Education and Science.

[*Hacker's diary continues – Ed.*]

August 19th

Today Humphrey and I discussed yesterday's meeting.

And it was now clear to me that I had to get out of the commitment that I had made. Quite clearly, Transport Supremo is a title that's not worth having.

I said to Humphrey that we had to find a way to force the PM's hand.

'Do you mean "we" plural – or do Supremos now use the royal pronoun?'

He was gloating. So I put the issue to him fair and square. I explained that I meant both of us, unless he wanted the DAA to be stuck with this problem.

As Humphrey clearly had no idea at all how to force the PM's hand. I told him how it's done. If you have to go for a politician's jugular, go for his constituency.

I told Bernard to get me a map and the local municipal directory of the PM's constituency.

Humphrey was looking puzzled. He couldn't see what I was proposing to do. But I had to put it to him in acceptably euphemistic language. 'Humphrey,' I said, 'I need your advice. Is it possible that implementing a national transport policy could have unfortunate local repercussions? Necessary, of course, in the wider national interest but painful to the borough affected!'

He caught on at once. 'Ah. Yes, indeed Minister,' he replied. 'Inevitable, in fact.' And he brightened up considerably.

'And if the affected borough was represented in the House by a senior member of the government – a very senior member of the government – the *most* senior member of the government . . .?'

Humphrey nodded gravely. 'Embarrassing,' he murmured. 'Deeply embarrasing.' But his eyes were gleaming.

In due course Bernard obtained the street map of the PM's constituency, and a street directory, and he found a relevant section in the business guide too. Once we studied the map, it was all plain sailing!

First we found a park. Humphrey noticed that it was near the railway station, and reminded me that one requirement of a national transport policy is to bring bus stations nearer to railway stations.

So, with deep regret, I made my first recommendation: *Build a bus station on Queen Charlotte's Park*. Someone has to suffer in the national interest, alas!

Second, we found a reference to a big bus repair shop, in the street Directory. It seemed to us that it would be more economical to integrate bus and train repairs. There would undoubtedly be a great saving. So our second recommendation was *Close the bus repair shop.*

Then it struck me that the PM's constituency is in commuter country. And we know, of course, that commuter trains run at a loss. They are only really used at rush hours. This means that commuters are, in effect, subsidised.

'Is this fair?' I asked Humphrey. He agreed that this was indeed an injustice to non-commuters. So we made our third recommendation: *Commuters to pay full economic fares.*

Sadly this will double the price of commuter tickets, but you can't make an omelette without breaking eggs.[1]

Humphrey noted that the PM's constituency contained several railway stations – British Rail as well as the Underground. He reminded me that some people take the view that areas with reasonable rail services don't need an evening bus service as well. I regard this as an extremely persuasive view. Accordingly, we made our fourth recommendation. *Stop all bus services after 6.30 p.m.*

We then moved on to consider what to do with all the remaining land after the removal of the bus station into the park.

We had to rack our brains on this matter for a while, but eventually we realised that the whole area seemed very short of parking space for container lorries. Especially at night. So fifth we recommended: *Container lorry park on bus station site.*

Regretfully, on closer study, the map revealed that building a new container lorry park would mean widening the access road. Indeed, it appears that the western half of the swimming baths might have to be filled in. But we could see no alternative: *Widen the access road to the bus station site* was our sixth and last recommendation.

We sat back and considered our list of recommendations. These had nothing whatever to do with the PM personally, of course. They were simply the local consequences of the broad national strategy.

However, I decided to write a paper which would be sent to Number Ten for the PM's personal attention. The PM would undoubtedly wish to be informed of the constituency implications and as a loyal Minister and dutiful colleague I owe this to the PM. Among other things!

[1] Originally said by Frederick the Great, King Frederick II of Prussia.

Humphrey raised one other area of concern. 'It would be awful, Minister, if the press got hold of all this. After all, lots of other boroughs are likely to be affected. There'd be a national outcry.'

I asked if he thought there was any danger of the press getting hold of the story.

'Well,' he said, 'they're very clever at getting hold of things like this. Especially if there's lots of copies.'

A good point. Humphrey's a bloody nuisance most of the time, but I must say that he's a good man to have on your side in a fight.

'Oh dear,' I replied. 'This *is* a problem, because I'll have to copy all my Cabinet colleagues with this note. Their constituencies are bound to be affected as well, of course.'

Humphrey reassured me on this point. He said that we must hope for the best. If it *were* leaked, with all those copies, no one could *ever* discover who leaked it. And as it happened, he was lunching today with Peter Martell of *The Times*.

I found this very reassuring.

I told him not to do anything that I wouldn't do. He told me that I could rely on him.

I'm sure I can.

I wonder how he got on.

[*Sir Humphrey's account of lunch with Peter Martell has been found in his private diary. – Ed.*]

> 19/viii
>
> Lunched with the chap from Printing House Square, and mentioned the recent rumours of the integrated national transport policy.
>
> His first reaction was one of boredom with this hoary old chestnut. Quite a natural reaction, really. But he became

Lunched with the chap from Printing House Square, and mentioned the recent rumours of the integrated national transport policy.

His first reaction was one of boredom with this hoary old chestnut. Quite a natural reaction, really. But he became interested when I hinted of the rumours that the policy may have several unwelcome side-effects.

1 Job loss from integration of the railway terminals.
2 Job loss from joint repair shops.
3 Job loss from streamlining of services.
4 Reduction of bus and train services – causing job loss.

Peter realised that this could be rather a large story, especially in view of the rumours that one of the areas to suffer most will be the PM's own constituency. I can't imagine how these rumours got around.

He asked for hard facts, and I admonished him. He persisted, explaining to me that newspapers are not like the Government – if they make statements they have to be able to prove that they are true.

He pressed me for news of a White Paper or a Green Paper. I gave no help. But I did have to confirm that there is in existence a confidential note from Hacker to the PM with similar notes to all twenty-one of his Cabinet colleagues.

'Oh that's all right then,' he said cheerfully. 'Are *you* going to show it to me or shall I get it from one of your colleagues?'

I reproved him. I explained that it was a confidential document. It would be grossly improper to betray it to anyone, let alone a journalist.

The only way he could possibly obtain a copy of such a document would be if somebody left it lying around by mistake. The chances of that happening are remote, of course.

[*It seems, from Sir Humphrey's account that he even wrote his private diary in such a way as to prevent it being used as evidence against him. But Peter Martell's subsequent publication of the full details of the confidential note, only one day later, suggests that Sir Humphrey had carelessly left his own copy lying around. – Ed.*]

August 21st

Humphrey did his job well. The full disclosure of my seven-point plan for the Prime Minister's constituency appeared in *The Times* yesterday. I must say I had a jolly good laugh about it. By 10.30 a.m. I'd received the expected summons for a chat with Sir Mark Spencer at Number Ten. (The PM's still abroad.)

I went this morning, and M.S. came straight to the point.

'I thought I ought to tell you that the PM isn't very pleased.' He waved *The Times* at me. 'This story.'

I agreed with him heartily. 'Yes, absolutely shocking. I wasn't pleased either.'

'There's obviously been a leak,' he murmured, eyeing me.

'Terrible. Can't trust any of my Cabinet colleagues nowadays.'

This wholehearted agreement threw him momentarily off guard, I think. 'Who are you saying it was?' he asked.

I lowered my voice and explained that I wouldn't want to name names, but as for one or two of my Cabinet colleagues . . . well! I left it at that. Looks speak louder than words sometimes.

He didn't want to leave it there. 'But what are you suggesting?'

I immediately backtracked. I was enjoying myself hugely. 'Well,' I said, 'it may *not* have been one of them, of course. I did send the paper here to Number Ten – could there be a leak *here* somewhere, do you think?'

Sir M was not amused. 'The PM's office does not leak.'

'Of course not,' I said quickly. 'Perish the thought.'

We all leak of course. That's what the lobby correspondents are there for. However, we all prefer to call it 'flying a kite.'

Sir Mark continued. 'It wasn't only the fact of the leak that was disturbing. It was the implications of the proposals.'

I agreed that the implications were indeed disturbing, which was why I had written a special paper for the PM. National transport policies are bound to have disturbing implications. He disagreed. He insisted that the Transport Policy will not have such implications.

'It will,' I said.

'It won't,' he said. Such is the intellectual cut and thrust to be found at the centre of government.

'Didn't you read what it said?' I asked.

'What it *said* is not what it will *be*,' he replied very firmly. 'I thought perhaps you'd like to see this.' And he handed me a newspaper, one of the London suburban weeklies.

It was the local paper from the PM's constituency.

P.M. Steps In to Stop Transport Re-organisation Proposals

BY NORMAN POTTER

Rumours that services and jobs were threatened in this constituency were scotched today. Apparently the P.M. has given a firm directive to transport supremo designate Jim Hacker.

This was certainly news to me.

'I've had no directive from the PM,' I said.

'You have now.' What a curious way to get a directive from the PM. 'I'm afraid this leak, whoever it comes from, is a verbatim report of a confidential minute dictated by the Prime Minister in Ottawa. So it looks as though the national transport policy will need some rethinking, doesn't it?'

This leak was a skilful counter-move by the PM. I started to explain to Sir Mark that rethinking the policy would be difficult, but he interrupted me unceremoniously.

'I think the PM's view is that Ministers are there to do difficult jobs. Assuming that they wish to remain as Ministers.'

Tough talk. I got the message.

I hastened to assure him that if the policy needed rethinking then I would rethink it until it was well and truly rethought.

Before I left I asked him how the leak had got into the paper. The PM's own local paper. He assured me that he had no idea, but that the PM's office does not leak.

'Shocking, though, isn't it?' he added 'You can't trust anyone nowadays.'

August 22nd

Another meeting with Humphrey. We appeared to be back to square one.

I was somewhat downcast, as I still appeared to be landed with this ghastly job. To my surprise Humphrey was in good spirits.

'It's all going excellently, Minister,' he explained. 'We shall now produce the other kind of non-proposal.'

I asked him what he had in mind.

'The high-cost high-staff kind of proposal. We now suggest a British National Transport Authority, with a full structure of Regional Boards, Area Councils, local offices, liaison committees – the lot. Eighty thousand staff, and a billion pounds a year budget.'

'The Treasury will have a fit,' I said.

'Precisely. And the whole matter will certainly be handed back to the Department of Transport.'

I was entranced. I asked him to do me a paper with full staff and costing details and a specimen annual budget.

He was way ahead of me. He immediately produced the very document from his folder. 'And there's a one page summary of the front,' he smiled smugly. Well, he was entitled to be smug!

I told him he was wonderful. He told me it was nothing.

I sat back and glanced through the proposal. It was splendid stuff.

'My goodness,' I reflected, 'if the press were to get hold of *this* . . . eh?'

Humphrey smiled. 'They'll soon be setting up another leak enquiry.'

Bernard was immediately anxious. 'Not really?'

'Bound to.'

'But . . . wouldn't that be embarrassing?'

I was surprised to see that Bernard didn't know the rules of the leak enquiry game. Leak enquiries are never embarrassing because they never actually happen. Leak enquiries are for setting up, not for actually conducting. Members may be appointed, but they hardly ever meet more than once. They certainly never report.

I asked Bernard, 'How many leak enquiries can you recall that named the culprit?'

'In round figures,' added Humphrey.

Bernard thought for a moment. 'Well, if you want it in round figures . . .' He thought again. 'None.'

The right answer. They *can't* report. For two reasons:

1 If the leak came from a civil servant it's not *fair* to publish it. The politicians are supposed to take the rap, that's what they're there for.

2 If the leak came from a politician it's not *safe* to publish it, because he will then promptly disclose all the other leaks he knows of that came from his Cabinet colleagues.

I explained all this to Bernard.

Then Humphrey chimed in. 'There's a third reason. The most important of all. The main reason why it's too dangerous to publish the results of an enquiry is because most leaks come from Number Ten. The ship of state is the only ship that leaks from the top.'

Humphrey was quite right, of course. Since the problem, more often than not, is a leaky PM – as in this case – it's not easy to get the evidence and impossible to publish it if you do.

And by a curious coincidence, a journalist arrived to see me this very morning, shortly after our meeting. Humphrey, most considerately, left a spare copy of our latest high-cost proposal lying around on my desk. I'm awfully absentminded, I'm always leaving bits of paper lying around, forgetting where I put them – the upshot was that after the journalist had left my office I couldn't find my spare copy anywhere. Extraordinary!

August 24th

It all came to a head today.

Humphrey and I were summoned – together this time – to a meeting at Number Ten. We were ushered into the Cabinet Secretary's office, where Sir Arnold and Sir Mark sat at the far end of a very long room. I think they were trying to intimidate us. But Humphrey and I are made of sterner stuff.

We greeted them cheerfully, and I sat in one of the armchairs in the conversation area. As a Minister of the Crown they were all my servants (nominally, at least) so they could not insist on a desk-bound interview. At my suggestion they joined me in Sir Arnold's armchairs. But he opened the batting. 'Another leak,' he said. 'This is extremely serious.'

'There has indeed been another leak,' I agreed. 'I can't think how it occurred! Our high-cost proposal was all over this morning's papers.'

Humphrey and I agreed earnestly that this new leak was indeed extremely serious.

'It is almost approaching a disciplinary level,' said Sir Arnold.

'I do agree,' I said, 'don't you, Humphrey?'

He nodded emphatically. 'Indeed, if only one could find the culprits it would be a most serious matter for them.'

Sir Mark piped up. He said he could help with that. He thought that if he were to use his influence he could achieve a disclosure from *The Times* of how they got hold of our original transport plans.

I shook Humphrey up a bit by offering to help further.

'Are you sure, Minister?' He sounded a warning note.

'Oh yes,' I said. 'In fact I'm confident that I could find out how the press got hold of the leak about the Prime Minister's opposition to our original plans. Of course, if it transpires that the PM's own office leaks, then that would be even more serious than a leak in a cabinet minister's private office, wouldn't it? The security implications alone . . .'

I let that threat hang in the air, and sat back.

'Ah,' said Sir Mark.

There was a pause while everyone thought and rethought their positions. I felt I had the initiative, so I continued: 'In fact, perhaps we ought to bring in the police or MI5 – after all, the implications of a leak at Number Ten are really very serious indeed.'

Arnold fought back. 'Nevertheless, our first priority must be to investigate the original leak.' He tried to insist.

I contradicted him flatly. 'No. Our first priority must be to track down the leak involving the PM.'

He really couldn't argue with that. And he didn't. He just sat in silence and looked at me. So after a moment, having won the Battle of the Leak Enquiries, I turned to the matter of the Transport Policy.

'At all events,' I said, summing up the situation, 'you will appreciate that the public outcry in response to all these leaks makes it very difficult for me to develop a national transport policy within the DAA.'

Sir Humphrey agreed vigorously. 'The time is unripe. The climate is unpropitious. The atmosphere is unfavourable.'

'And,' I nodded, 'the only two lines of approach are now blocked.'

Again there was a silence. Again Arnold and Mark stared at me. Then they stared at each other. Defeat stared at them both. Finally Sir Arnold resigned himself to the inevitable.

But he tried to put as good a face on it as he could. He raised the oldest idea as if it were the latest inspiration. 'I wonder,' he addressed himself to Sir Mark, 'if it might not be wiser to take the whole matter back to the Department of Transport?'

I seized on the suggestion. 'Now that, Arnold,' I said, flattering him fulsomely, 'is a brilliant idea.'

'I wish I'd thought of that,' said Humphrey wistfully.

So we were all agreed.

But Sir Mark was still worried. 'There remains the question of the leaks,' he remarked.

'Indeed there does,' I agreed. 'And in my view we should treat this as a matter of utmost gravity. So I have a proposal.'

'Indeed?' enquired Sir Arnold.

'Will you recommend to the PM,' I said, in my most judicial voice, 'that we set up an immediate leak enquiry?'

Sir Arnold, Sir Mark and Sir Humphrey responded in grateful unison. 'Yes Minister,' replied the three knights.

5
The Whisky Priest

September 1st

A most significant and upsetting event has just taken place. It is Sunday night. Annie and I are in our London flat, having returned early from the constituency.

I had a mysterious phone call as I walked in through the door. I didn't know who it was from. All the man said was that he was an Army officer and that he had something to tell me that he wouldn't divulge on the phone.

We arranged an appointment for late this evening. Annie read the Sunday papers, and I read *The Wilderness Years*, one of my favourite books.

The man arrived very late for our appointment. I began to think that something had happened to him. By the time he'd arrived my fantasies were working overtime – perhaps because of *The Wilderness Years*.

'Remember Churchill,' I said to Annie. 'During all his wilderness years he got all his information about our military inadequacy and Hitler's war machine from army officers. So all the time he was in the wilderness he leaked stories to the papers and embarrassed the government. That's what I could do.'

I realised, as I spoke, that I'd chosen inappropriate words to express my feelings. I felt a little ridiculous as Annie said, 'But you're in the government.' Surely she could see what I *meant*!

Anyway, the man finally arrived. He introduced himself as Major Saunders. He was about forty years old, and wore the *de riguur* slightly shabby baggy blue pinstripe suit. Like all these chaps he looked like an overgrown prep school pupil.

He was not a frightfully good conversationalist to start with. Or perhaps he was just rather overawed to meet a statesman such as myself.

I introduced him to Annie and offered him a drink.

'Thanks,' he said.

'Scotch?'

'Thanks.'

I told him to sit down.

'Thanks.'

I told him there was no need to keep thanking me.

'Thanks,' he said, then corrected himself. 'Sorry.'

Annie told him there was no need to apologise either.

'Sorry,' he said. 'I mean, thanks. I mean . . .'

Clearly my eminence was reducing this chap to a sort of jelly.

Annie offered to go and let us chaps talk in private, but for some reason he seemed anxious for her to stay. Can't think why. Anyway, he asked if she could stay and of course I agreed.

'I have no secrets from Annie,' I explained. 'I tell her everything.'

'Several times, normally,' she added cheerfully.

I do *wish* she wouldn't make jokes like that. People might think that she means them.

I decided to establish whether the slightly cloak-and-dagger air about our meeting was, in fact, necessary. 'Is this matter highly confidential?' I asked.

'Well, fairly,' he replied, rather on edge. Clearly 'fairly' was a bit of traditional British understatement.

'Shall I turn on the radio?' I offered.

He seemed surprised. 'Why – is there something good on?'

I don't know what they teach these army chaps nowadays. I explained that I was suggesting that we play the radio to avoid being bugged. He asked if it was likely that we were being bugged. How does one know the answer to that? But then Annie reminded me that, as I am the Minister in charge of bugging politicians, it wasn't awfully likely.

But Saunders was quite clear that he didn't want our conversation to be on the record, even though I made it clear that I would take notes at the meeting if necessary (which indeed it was). He began by saying that what he was about to tell me he was telling me on a personal basis.

I asked him what he meant, precisely. I do like clarity in language.

'I'm telling you personally,' he repeated. 'Not as Minister of Administrative Affairs.'

I could *sort of* see what he meant. But, on the other hand, I *am* Minister of Administrative Affairs. I sought further clarification.

'Yes, I know you are,' he said. 'But I'm not telling you in that role. I'm telling you as a journalist.'

'Are you a journalist?' I was surprised. 'I thought you were an army officer.'

'No – *you* are a journalist.'

'I'm a Minister.'

'But – what were you before you became a Minister?'

'Your starter for ten, no conferring,' interrupted Annie facetiously. She's always watched too much television and has always had a rather silly infatuation with Bamber Gascoigne merely because he's charming and clever.

In any case, I'd now seen what Saunders was driving at. I put it into simple language, so that we were both clear about what we were both saying.

'You're telling me that what you're telling me – and, incidentally, I don't yet *know* what you're telling me – but, whatever it is that you're telling me, you're telling me as the former Editor of *Reform*. Is that it?'

'Yes,' he replied. 'You were a very fine editor.'

'I wouldn't say that,' I said modestly.

'You've often said that,' said Annie. Another of her bloody jokes. Sometimes she's more hindrance than help.

We still hadn't found a basis for my receipt of his confidential information. So I had to pursue our talks about talks, as it were. 'How,' I wanted to know, 'do I prevent myself from knowing what you are telling me as a former journalist?'

I couldn't see how I could help the Minister knowing if *I* knew.

'I think he means it's a question of hats, dear,' said Annie. Of course it was. Perfectly bloody obvious. I tried to disguise my irritation.

'Fine,' I said, smiling. 'I'm not wearing my Ministerial hat tonight. I understand that. But . . .' and here I think I impressed him with the solemnity of my high office under the Crown, '. . . I must warn you: if I need to tell myself what you tell me, I won't hesitate to do my duty and see that I am properly informed.'

'Fine,' agreed Major Saunders.

It seemed that at last we had some basis on which to open up our conversation. I waited with bated breath.

He took a large gulp of his whisky, put down his glass firmly on the coffee table, and fixed me with a bloodshot stare. 'Who is in charge of selling British weapons to foreigners?'

'Bzzzzz. Hacker, LSE,' said Annie. I silenced her with a filthy look. Then I waited for more from Saunders. After all, he'd requested the meeting because he'd had something to *tell* me, not to ask me.

Saunders realised the ball was still in his court. 'You wrote an article in *Reform* about the sale of British weapons to undesirable foreign buyers.'

I remembered it well. I had called it 'The Dreadful Trade'. In it I argued – as I have always argued – that while it is wholly patriotic to manufacture arms for our defence and even for the defence of our allies, even though some of our allies are scarcely commendable people, we should never sell British weapons to buttress enemies of the realm or Nazi-style dictators. I repeated the gist of my argument to Saunders. He nodded. 'What about terrorists?' he asked.

'Or terrorists,' I added firmly.

He nodded again. I began to have the feeling that I was being led somewhere, as if by a good interrogator or a prosecuting counsel. But I still had no idea of the enormity of the shock that he had in store for me.

'As you know,' he began to explain, 'I recently returned from Rome.' He had told me on the phone that he'd been there as part of a NATO military delegation. 'While I was there I was shown something that they'd captured in a raid on a terrorist HQ. It was a computerised bomb detonator. Very new, very secret and very lethal.'

'Who showed it to you?' I asked.

'I can't possibly tell you. An absolute confidence.'

I was mildly interested in this computerised detonator thing and invited him to continue.

'You set it to calculate the weight of the victim, the speed of his car and so on, to be sure of getting him. And you can reprogramme it remotely by radio after setting it.'

'Gosh,' I said, walking straight into it. 'You don't connect the Italians with that sort of technology, do you?'

'It wasn't made in Italy,' he countered swiftly. 'It was made here.'

It took me a moment or two to grasp the full implications of what he was saying.

'Here?'

'Yes. Under a Ministry of Defence contract.'

I could hardly believe what he was telling me. As a matter of fact, I still find it incredible. And appalling. British weapons being used by Italian Red Terrorists.

I asked him how they got them.

'That's what I want to know,' he answered.

I asked him who else he'd told. He says he's told no one, because he can't. 'If I reported it officially I'd have to disclose the source. But I thought if I told someone near the top of government . . .'

'At the top,' I corrected him firmly.

He paused and nodded. Then he went on to explain that someone at the top of government would be able, in his opinion, to find out how these weapons are being supplied. Because the investigation would have to start here in Britain, and at top level.

I couldn't see how he thought I was to do this, since he had made it clear that he was telling me on a personal basis.

He spelt it out to me. 'You see, now you know personally, even if you don't know officially, you can use your personal knowledge to start official enquiries to get official confirmation of personal suspicions so that what you now know personally but not officially you will then know officially as well as personally.'

After a year in government I can now make sense of, and recall such sentences. Perhaps in another year I'll be speaking like that myself.

'You're not related to Sir Humphrey Appleby, are you?' I enquired semi-humorously. But no. This is not a family talent, this is the language of the governing classes as they try – as always – to have everything both ways.

Saunders heaved a sigh of relief, finished the rest of his Scotch, and remarked that he had just had to tell somebody.

'Absolutely,' I agreed, at my most understanding. 'Well, now I know. Personally.' Two could play this game.

'Marvellous. Going to do something about it, aren't you?'

'Indeed I am,' I agreed emphatically. 'Oh yes. Definitely.'

'And right away?'

'Right away.' I was employing my most decisive manner.

'*What* are you going to do?'

I hadn't actually expected such a direct question. I couldn't see what that had to do with him. He'd done his duty by informing me, it's not for serving army officers to question Ministers of the Crown. Anyway that's the sort of irritating question that you tend to get from backbench MPs and other awkward busybodies who keep wanting to find out what the government's doing.

However, both he and Annie were sitting waiting for an answer. I had to say something. 'Well, I'm going to think about what you've told me.' They didn't look too impressed. 'Right away!' I added decisively.

'And then?' Persistent bugger.

'And then I'm going to consider various courses of action, without delay.'

He insisted on seeking clarification. Or trying to pin me down. 'You're going to take action without delay?'

'I'm going to *consider* taking action without delay.' I thought I'd better be clear about this.

'Are *you* related to Sir Humphrey Appleby?' enquired Annie.

I rose above it, ignored her, and offered Major Saunders another drink. He declined, stood up preparatory to leaving, and asked for my assurance that he could rely on me to tackle this shocking matter. Naturally I gave him that assurance.

After he left Annie and I discussed him and his extraordinary information. I asked Annie what she made of it.

She didn't reply directly. She just told me that I really was going to do something about it wasn't I?

And I certainly am. If it's true. But I find it hard to believe. Could it happen? It couldn't happen! Could it? I mean, it's not just that it shouldn't but it couldn't. And even if it could, it wouldn't. Would it?

I've just played that last paragraph back. Perhaps I *am* related to Sir Humphrey Appleby.

September 2nd

Today I had a serious conversation with Humphrey. Perhaps the most serious conversation that I have ever had or will ever have.

I'm still not quite sure what to make of it. Or him.

He came in for his regular Monday morning meeting with me. I hurried through all the usual items on the agenda, and then set the tone for the discussion that I intended to have.

'Humphrey,' I began, 'there is something that I must talk to you about. Something that concerns one deeply. Really profoundly important.'

He enquired whether I was referring to the amendment to the Administrative order on stock control in government establishments, or the procedures for the renewal of local authority leaseholds in Special Development Areas.

This is the level at which he operates. But I was patient. 'No Humphrey,' I explained, 'I'm concerned about a great issue of life and death.'

'Shouldn't that wait till after work?' he asked. You can see what I'm dealing with.

'It is work.'

'Really?' He was surprised. 'Then please go on.'

I asked him how British arms manufacturers sell arms to foreigners. He explained the whole system to me. The manufacturer has to get an export licence from the Department of Trade. Both private companies and government agencies sell arms abroad. They usually sell to foreign governments, but sometimes they sell to arms dealers. Third parties. In other words, perhaps a little man in Manchester buys on behalf of a party in the Channel Islands who has a contract in Luxembourg, and so on.

So I wanted to know if there was any way of controlling who the arms are really going to. Humphrey assured me that there *is* control. The dealer has to provide a document known as an end-user certificate. This certificate must have a signature on it from the ultimate customer who is an approved user acceptable to HMG.[1]

I found myself wondering if this end-user certificate is a real guarantee. I wonder if Humphrey would be surprised if, for instance, an aircraft carrier turned up in the Central African Republic.

[*Sir Humphrey would undoubtedly have been surprised, as would everybody else, as the Central African Republic is one thousand miles inland. – Ed.*]

Sir Humphrey stated that it was 'officially impossible' for weapons to turn up in non-approved hands. 'There is stringent security, there are rigorous inspection procedures, and meticulous scrutiny.'

Officially impossible. I know what that phrase means. It means that it's all a façade.

I challenged him with this. He smiled benignly and inclined his head a little. 'I think perhaps this conversation should stop here Minister, don't you?'

I refused to play the game this time. 'No,' I said. 'But it is as I thought. Last night a confidential source disclosed to me that British arms are being sold to Italian Red Terrorist Groups.'

He nodded gravely. 'I see. May I ask who the confidential source was?'

I was staggered. 'Humphrey! I just said that it's confidential.'

He was unashamed. 'Oh I'm sorry, Minister, I naturally assumed that meant you were going to tell me.'

---

[1] Her Majesty's Government.

He waited. I waited too. As I sat there, quietly watching him, I observed that he did not seem to be awfully worried about the information that I had just given him. So I questioned him on this. And indeed, he seemed to find it quite unremarkable.

'These things happen all the time, Minister. It's not our problem.'

'Robbery with violence happens all the time. Doesn't that worry you?'

'No Minister. Home Office problem.'

I was almost speechless. He seemed to see himself only as an official, not as a citizen. Of course, that is the hat that he wears when at the office advising me, but there are moral issues involved.

'We are letting terrorists get hold of murderous weapons,' I expostulated.

'We're not.'

I was confused. 'Well, who is?'

'Who knows?' He was at his most bland. 'The Department of Trade? The Ministry of Defence? The Foreign Office?'

I was getting impatient. This was wilful stupidity, no doubt about it. '*We*, Humphrey. The British Government. Innocent lives are being endangered by British weapons in the hands of terrorists.'

'Only Italian lives, not British lives.'

'There may be British tourists in Italy,' I replied, letting the wider issue go temporarily by default. (The wider issue being that no man is an island.)[1]

'British tourists? Foreign Office problem.'

I was wearying of this juvenile buck-passing. 'Look Humphrey,' I said, 'we have to do something.'

'With respect, Minister . . .' the gloves were coming off now, '. . . we have to do *nothing*.'

It seemed to me that he was somehow suggesting that doing nothing was an active rather than a passive course. So I asked him to elaborate.

He was perfectly willing to do so. 'The sale of arms abroad is one of those areas of government which we do not examine too closely.'

I couldn't accept that. I told him that I have to examine this area, now that I know.

He said that I could say that I didn't know.

---

[1] 'No man is an Island, entire of itself . . . Any man's death diminishes me, because I am involved in Mankind; And therefore never send to know for whom the bell tolls; it tolls for thee.' – John Donne.

I wanted to be quite clear what he was saying that I should be saying. 'Are you suggesting that I should lie?'

'Not you, no,' came the enigmatic response.

'Who should lie, then?' I asked.

'Sleeping dogs, Minister.'

We were getting no further. Trying to have an argument with Humphrey can be like trying to squash a bowlful of porridge with your fist. I told him that I intended to raise the question and take the matter further as I was not satisfied with such reassurances as Sir Humphrey had been able to give me.

Now he looked upset. Not about bombs or terrorists or innocent lives, but about taking the matter further. 'Please Minister, I beg of you!'

I waited for him to explain further. Perhaps I would now learn something. And I did. But not what I expected.

'Minister, two basic rules of government: Never look into anything you don't have to. And never set up an enquiry unless you know in advance what its findings will be.'

He was still obsessed with rules of government, in the face of a moral issue of these proportions. 'Humphrey, I can't believe it. We're talking about good and evil.'

'Ah. Church of England problem.'

I was not amused. 'No Humphrey, *our* problem. We are discussing right and wrong.'

'You may be Minister,' he replied smoothly, 'but I'm not. It would be a serious misuse of government time.'

I thought at first that he was joking. But he wasn't! He was serious, absolutely serious.

'Can't you see,' I begged emotionally, 'that selling arms to terrorists is wrong? Can't you *see* that?'

He couldn't. 'Either you sell arms or you don't,' was his cold, rational reply. 'If you sell them, they will inevitably end up with people who have the cash to buy them.'

I could see the strength of that argument. But terrorists had to be prevented, somehow, from getting hold of them.

Humphrey seemed to find this a ridiculous and/or an impractical approach. He smiled patronisingly. 'I suppose we could put a sort of government health warning on all the rifle butts. NOT TO BE SOLD TO TERRORISTS. Do you think that would help?' I was speechless. 'Or better still, WARNING: THIS GUN CAN SERIOUSLY DAMAGE YOUR HEALTH.'

I didn't laugh. I told him that it was rather shocking, in my view, that he could make light of such a matter. I demanded a straight answer. I asked him if he was saying that we should close our eyes to something that's as morally wrong as this business.

He sighed. Then he replied, with slight irritation. 'If you *insist* on making me discuss moral issues, perhaps I should point out that something is either morally wrong or it is not. It can't be slightly morally wrong.'

I told him not to quibble.

He quibbled again. 'Minister, Government isn't about morality.'

'Really? Then what is it about?'

'It's about stability. Keeping things going, preventing anarchy, stopping society falling to bits. Still being here tomorrow.'

'But what *for*?' I asked.

I had stumped him. He didn't understand my question. So I spelt it out for him.

'What is the ultimate purpose of Government, if it isn't for doing good?'

This notion was completely meaningless to him. 'Government isn't about good and evil, it's only about order and chaos.'

I know what he means. I know that all of us in politics have to swallow things we don't believe in sometimes, vote for things that we think are wrong. I'm a realist, not a boy scout. Otherwise I could never have reached Cabinet level. I'm not naïve. I know that nations just act in their own interest. But . . . there has to be a sticking point somewhere. Can it really be in order for Italian terrorists to get British-made bomb detonators?

I don't see how it can be. But, more shocking still, Humphrey just didn't seem to care. I asked him how that was possible?

Again he had a simple answer. 'It's not my job to care. That's what politicians are for. It's my job to carry out government policy.'

'Even if you think it's wrong?'

'Almost all government policy is wrong,' he remarked obligingly, 'but frightfully well carried out.'

This was all too urbane for my liking. I had an irresistible urge to get to the bottom of this great moral issue, once and for all. This 'just obeying orders' mentality can lead to concentration camps. I wanted to nail this argument.

'Humphrey, have you ever known a civil servant resign on a matter of principle?'

Now, *he* was shocked. 'I should think not! What a suggestion!'

How remarkable. This is the only suggestion that I had made in this conversation that had shocked my Permanent Secretary. I sat back in my chair and contemplated him. He waited, presumably curious to see what other crackpot questions I would be asking.

'I realise, for the very first time,' I said slowly, 'that you are committed purely to means, never to ends.'

'As far as I am concerned, Minister, and all my colleagues, there is no difference between means and ends.'

'If you believe that,' I told him, 'you will go to Hell.'

There followed a long silence. I thought he was reflecting on the nature of the evil to which he had committed himself. But no! After a while, realising that I was expecting a reply, he observed with mild interest, 'Minister, I had no idea that you had a theological bent.'

My arguments had clearly left him unaffected. 'You are a moral vacuum, Humphrey,' I informed him.

'If you say so, Minister.' And he smiled courteously and inclined his head, as if to thank me for a gracious compliment.

Bernard had been in the room for the entire meeting so far, though taking very few minutes, I noticed. Unusually for him, he had not said a word. Now he spoke.

'It's time for your lunch appointment, Minister.'

I turned to him. 'You're keeping very quiet Bernard. What would you do about all this?'

'I'd keep very quiet Minister.'

The conversation had ground to a halt. I'd thrown every insult at Sir Humphrey that I could think of, and he had taken each one as a compliment. He appears to be completely amoral. Not immoral – he simply doesn't understand moral concepts. His voice broke in on my thoughts. 'So may we now drop this matter of arms sales?'

I told him that we may not. I told him that I would be telling the PM about it, in person. And I told Bernard to make the appointment for me, as it is just the sort of thing the PM wants to know about.

Humphrey intervened. 'I assure you, Minister, it is just the sort of thing the Prime Minister desperately wants not to know about.'

I told him we'd see. And I left for lunch.

SIR BERNARD WOOLLEY RECALLS:[1]
I well remember that I felt fearfully downcast after that fateful meeting. Because I couldn't help wondering if the Minister was right. I voiced this

[1] In conversation with the Editors.

fear to old Humphrey. 'Most unlikely,' he replied. 'What about?'

I explained that I too was worried about ends versus means. I asked Humphrey if I too would end up as a moral vacuum. His reply surprised me. 'I hope so,' he told me. 'If you work hard enough.'

This made me feel more melancholy than before. At that time, you see, I still believed that if it was our job to carry out government policies we ought to believe in them.

Sir Humphrey shook his head and left the room. Later that day I received a memorandum from him. I have it still.

Memorandum

From: The Permanent Secretary
To: B.W.

2/ix

I have been considering your question. Please bear in mind the following points.

I have served eleven governments in the past thirty years. If I had believed in all their policies I would have been:

(i) passionately committed to keeping out of the Common Market

(ii) passionately committed to going into the Common Market.

Memorandum
From: The Permanent Secretary
To: B.W.
I have been considering your question. Please bear in mind the following points.

118

I have served eleven governments in the past thirty years. If I had believed in all their policies I would have been:
  1) passionately committed to keeping out of the Common Market.
  2) passionately committed to going into the Common Market.
  3) utterly convinced of the rightness of nationalising steel.
  4) utterly convinced of the rightness of denationalising steel.
  5) utterly convinced of the rightness of re-nationalising steel.
  6) fervently committed to retaining capital punishment.
  7) ardently committed to abolishing capital punishment.
  8) a Keynesian.
  9) a Friedmanite.
  10) a grammar school preserver.
  11) a grammar school destroyer.
  12) a nationalisation maniac.
  13) a privatisation freak.
  14) a stark, staring, raving schizophrenic.

H.A.

The following day he sent for me, to check that I was fully seized of his ideas and had taken them on board.

Of course, his argument was irrefutable. I freely admitted it. And yet I was *still* downcast. Because, as I explained to Appleby, I felt that I needed to believe in *something*.

He suggested that we should both believe in stopping Hacker from informing the PM.

Of course he was right. Once the PM knew of this business, there would have to be an enquiry. It would be like Watergate, in which, as you know, the investigation of a trivial break-in led to one ghastly revelation after another and finally to the downfall of a President. The Golden Rule is, was, always has been and always will be: Don't Lift Lids Off Cans of Worms.

'Everything is connected to everything else,' Sir Humphrey explained. 'Who said that?'

I ventured a guess that it might have been the Cabinet Secretary.

'Nearly right,' Sir Humphrey encouraged me. 'Actually, it was Lenin.'

He then set me the task – to stop my Minister from talking to the PM.

At first I couldn't see how this could be achieved, and was unwise enough to say. This earned me a sharp rebuke.

'Work it out,' he snapped. 'I thought you were supposed to be a high-flyer – or are you really a low-flyer supported by occasional gusts of wind?'

I could see that this was one of those make or break moments in one's career. I went off and had a quiet think, and I asked myself some questions.

  1 Could I stop my Minister from seeing the PM? Clearly not?
  2 Could Sir Humphrey? No.
  3 Could my friends in the Private Office at Number Ten? Or the Cabinet Office? No.

Therefore the approach had to be through the political side. I needed someone close to the PM, somone who was able to frighten Hacker.

Suddenly it was clear. There's only one figure whose job it is to put the frighteners on MPs – the Chief Whip.

I planned my strategy carefully. Hacker had asked me to phone the diary secretary in the PM's private office for him, to make an appointment. I worked out that if Sir Humphrey had a word with the Cabinet Secretary, he (the Cabinet Secretary) could have a word with the PM's diary secretary, then all of them could have a word with the Whip's office.

The Chief Whip would see the point at once. When Hacker arrived to see the PM the Chief Whip would meet him, and say that the PM was rather busy and had asked him to talk to Hacker instead.

I requested a meeting with Appleby, and told him of my plan. He nodded approvingly. So I lifted up his phone.

'What are you doing Bernard?' he asked.

'I thought you wanted to talk to the Cabinet Secretary, Sir Humphrey,' I replied with mock innocence.

He took the phone from me, and made the call. I sat and listened. When it was done Appleby replaced the receiver, sat back in his chair and eyed me speculatively.

'Tell me Bernard, do you – as his Private Secretary – feel obliged to tell the Minister of this conversation?'

'What conversation?' I replied.

He offered me a sherry, congratulated me, and told me that I would be a moral vacuum yet.

I believe that it was at this moment that my future was assured. From then on I was ear-marked as a future head of the Home Civil Service.

[*Hacker's diary continues. – Ed.*]

September 5th

I feel rather guilty and not a little stupid this evening. Also, somewhat concerned for my future. I just hope that Vic Gould [*The Chief Whip. – Ed.*] presents me in a favourable light to the PM next time my name is put forward for anything.

I think that Vic owes me a big favour after today. But he's a strange fellow and he may not see it that way.

I wasn't expecting to see him at all. My appointment was with the PM, at the House. When I got to the PM's office I found Vic Gould waiting there.

Vic is a tall imposing figure, with the white hair of an elder statesman, a face like a vulture and a manner that shifts at lightning speed from charm and soft soap to vulgar abuse. A party man to his fingertips.

He was a bit casual, I thought. He said that the PM was rather busy today and had asked him to see me instead.

I felt slightly insulted. I don't report to Vic. He may be responsible for party discipline but he's one of my colleagues, an equal member of this government. Actually, I had no idea that he was so close to the PM. Or maybe he isn't – maybe it's just that he persuaded the PM (who didn't know why I wanted the appointment) that it was a party matter rather than a political one. But what I can't work out is how did *Vic* know what I wanted? And how did the PM arrive at the decision that Vic should see me instead? Sometimes I really do feel a little paranoid.

As it turned out perhaps it's all for the best, *if* Vic can be believed. But can he? Can anybody?

Anyway, when Vic greeted me I refused to tell him what I'd come about. I couldn't see that arms sales to Italian terrorists was a matter for the Chief Whip.

He refused to take no for an answer. 'The PM has asked me to have a preliminary conversation with you, and write a background note. Save time later.'

I couldn't argue with that. So I told Vic that I'd been given this pretty dramatic information. And I told him the whole story of Italian Red Terrorists being supplied with top secret bomb detonators made in this country. In a government factory!

'And you feel you should tell the PM?'

I was astonished by the question. The PM is in charge of security. I could see no choice.

But Vic disagreed. 'I don't think it's something to burden the PM with. Let's hold it over, shall we?'

I asked if he *actually* meant to do nothing about it. He nodded, and said yes, that was his recommendation.

I refused to accept this, and insisted that the PM had to be told.

'If the PM were to be told,' said Vic carefully, 'there'd have to be an enquiry.'

That was my point. That was what I wanted.

But it was not what Vic wanted. He explained why. 'An enquiry might perhaps reveal that all sorts of undesirable and even hostile governments had been supplied with British-made arms.'

This remark shocked me. Not so much on account of its factual content, but because of the assumption that such matters should not be looked into.'

'Are you serious?' I asked.

'I said *perhaps*. Which would – perhaps – be highly embarrassing to some of our Cabinet colleagues. Foreign Secretary, Defence Secretary, Trade Secretary. And to the PM personally.'

I stuck to my guns. 'Doing what's right can be embarrassing. But that's not an argument for not doing it.'

Vic ignored that. 'You know we already sell arms to places like Syria, Chile and Iran?'

I did know. 'That's officially approved,' I explained, meaning that it was therefore beside the point.

'Quite,' agreed Vic. 'And you're happy about what they do with them?'

I hesitated. 'Well, obviously not entirely . . .'

'Either you're in the arms business or you're not,' said Vic with relentless logic.

At that point I became emotional. A big mistake. It's all right to pretend to be emotional, especially in front of the public (or even with the House if it's the right ploy for the moment) but with one's colleagues – especially a cold fish like Vic – it cuts no ice at all.

'If being in the arms business means being among criminals and murderers, then we should get out. It's immoral.'

Vic lost his temper. He glowered at me with a mixture of anger and contempt. 'Oh great. *Great!*'

I felt he really despised me. I could see him wondering how a boy scout like me had ever been allowed into the Cabinet. Or even into *politics.* 'And is it moral to put a hundred thousand British workers out of a job? And what about the exports? Two billion pounds a year down the tube for starters. And what about the votes? Where do you think the government places all these weapons contracts?'

'Marginal constituencies, obviously.'

'Exactly,' he said. QED, he implied.

But I still couldn't quite leave it alone. I tried again. 'Look Vic, all I'm saying is that now I know this is happening I have to tell the PM.'

'Why?'

'Why?' I couldn't understand the question. It seemed self-evident to me.

'Just because you've caught something nasty,' said Vic, 'why do you have to wander about breathing over everyone?'

While I was considering my answer – or to be precise, wondering if I really *had* an answer – he turned the anglepoise lamp on the desk in my direction. He wasn't *exactly* shining it in my eyes, but I did have the distinct feeling that I was being given the Third Degree.

And his next question did nothing to dilute the impression that I was under interrogation on account of suspect loyalty.

'Are you happy in the Cabinet?'

'Yes, of course I am.

'You want to stay in it?'

My heart sank into my boots. I couldn't speak. My loyalty was now in doubt. Oh my God! I nodded mutely.

'Well then?' He waited for me to say something.

I was sweating. And no longer thinking clearly enough. This was not the meeting that I had expected. I had expected to be on the attack. Instead I found myself fighting a desperate defensive. Suddenly my whole political future seemed to be on the line.

And I still stuck to my guns. I'm not quite sure why. I think I was confused, that's all.

'There is such a thing as duty,' I heard myself say rather pompously. 'There are times when you have to do what your conscience tells you.'

Vic lost his temper again. I could see why. Telling a Chief Whip that you have to follow your conscience really is like waving a red rag at a bull.

And this time it wasn't a quiet irritable loss of temper. It was the Big Shout, for which he is famous throughout the Palace of Westminster. He leapt to his feet. 'Oh for God's sake!' he yelled, obviously at the end of his tether.

His face came close to mine. Almost nose to nose. His angry bulging eyes were so near that they were slightly out of focus. He was utterly contemptuous of me now.

'Must you go around flashing your petty private little individual conscience? Do you think no one else has got one? Haven't you got a conscience about the survival of the government?'

'Of course I have,' I muttered, when the storm seemed to have abated temporarily.

He walked away, satisfied that at least I'd given one correct answer. 'Here's the PM on the verge of signing an international agreement on anti-terrorism . . .'

I interrupted, in self-defence. 'I didn't know about that,' I explained.

'There's a lot you don't know,' snapped Vic contemptuously.

[*It is not surprising that Hacker did not know about a new international anti-terrorist agreement. So far as we have been able to find out, there was none. Vic Gould presumably invented this on the spur of the moment. – Ed.*]

He came and sat beside me again. He tried to be patient. Or

rather, he looked as though he was trying to be patient. 'Can't you understand that it's essential to deal with the major policy aspects, rather than pick off a couple of little arms exporters and terrorist groups?'

I hadn't seen it like that. Furthermore, I realised that I'd better see it like that, and quickly, or else Vic would go on shouting at me all day. 'I suppose it is only a couple of little terrorist groups,' I said weakly.

'They can't kill *that* many people, can they?'

'I suppose not,' I agreed, with a little smile to show that I realised that perhaps I'd been a bit naïve.

But Vic had still not finished with the insults. He sneered at me again. 'And you want to blow it all in a fit of moral self-indulgence.'

Clearly moral self-indulgence was the most disgusting thing Vic had ever come across. I felt very small.

He sat back in his chair, sighed, then grinned at me and offered me a cigarette. And dropped the bombshell.

'After all,' he smiled, 'the PM is thinking of you as the next Foreign Secretary.'

I was astounded. Of course it's what I've always wanted, if Martin's ever kicked upstairs. But I didn't know the PM knew.

I declined his offer of a cigarette. He lit up, and relaxed. 'Still, if it's martydom you're after,' he shrugged, 'go ahead and press for an enquiry. Feel free to jeopardise everything we've all fought for and worked for together all these years.'

I hastily explained that that wasn't what I wanted at all, that of course it is appalling if terrorists are getting British bomb detonators but there's no question that (as Vic had so eloquently explained it) one has a *loyalty*, the common purpose, and things must be put in perspective.

He nodded. 'Of course,' he said, making a concession to my original point of view, 'if you were at the Ministry of Defence or the Board of Trade . . .'

I interrupted. 'Exactly. Absolutely. Ministry of Defence problem. Department of Trade problem. I see that now.' It's just what Humphrey had been trying to say to me, in fact.

We fell silent, both waiting sure that the problem was now resolved. Finally Vic asked if we could hold it over for the time being, so that we could avoid upsetting and embarrassing the PM.

I agreed that we could. 'In fact,' I admitted, rather ashamed of my naïvity, 'I'm sorry I mentioned it.'

'Good man,' said Vic paternally. I don't *think* he was being ironic, but you can never tell with Vic.

September 8th

Annie had spent the latter part of the week in the constituency, so I wasn't able to get her advice on my meeting with Vic until this weekend.

Not that I really needed advice. By today it was quite clear to me what I had to do. I explained to Annie over a nightcap of Scotch and water.

'On balance I thought the right thing was to let sleeping dogs lie. In the wider interest. As a loyal member of the government. Nothing to be gained by opening a whole can of worms.'

She argued, of course. 'But the Major said they were terrorists.'

I couldn't blame her for taking such a naïve approach. After all, even *I* had made the same mistake till I'd thought it all through properly.

'Yes,' I said. 'But we bombed Dresden. Everyone's a terrorist in a way, aren't they?'

'No,' she said firmly, and gave me a look which defied me to disagree with her.

I had overstated it a bit. 'No, well, but *metaphorically* they are,' I added. 'You ought to meet the Chief Whip, he *certainly* is.'

Annie pursued me. She didn't understand the wider interest, the more sophisticated level on which decisions like this have to be reached. 'But someone in Britain is giving bombs to murderers,' she reiterated.

'Not giving,' I corrected her. 'Selling.'

'That makes it okay, does it?'

I told her to be serious, and to think it through. I explained that an investigation could uncover all sorts of goings on.

She wasn't impressed with this argument.

'Ah, I see,' she smiled sadly. 'It's all right to investigate if you might catch one criminal, but not if you might catch lots of them.'

'Not if they're your Cabinet colleagues, that's right!' She'd got the point now. But she sighed and shook her head. Clearly, she had not yet taken my new line on board. So I persisted. I really wanted her to understand. And to agree.

'Annie, Government is a very complex business. There are conflicting considerations.'

'Like whether you do the right thing or the wrong thing?'

I was infuriated. I asked her what else she suggested that I could do. She told me to take a moral stand. I told her I'd already tried that. She told me I hadn't tried hard enough. I asked what *else* I could do. She told me to threaten resignation. I told her that they'd accept it.

And once out of office there's no going back. No one ever resigned on a matter of principle, except a few people with a death wish. Most resignations that are *said* to be based on principle are in reality based on hard-nosed political calculations.

'Resignation might be a sop to my conscience and to yours,' I explained, 'but it won't stop the arms supply to the terrorists.'

'It might,' she retorted, 'if you threaten to tell what you know.'

I considered that for a moment. But, in fact, what do I know? I don't know anything. At least, nothing I can prove. I've no hard facts at all. I know that the story is true simply because no one has denied it – but that's not proof. I explained all this to Annie, adding that therefore I was in somewhat of a fix.

She saw the point. Then she handed me a letter. 'I don't think you realise just how big a fix you're in. This arrived today. From Major Saunders.'

> *12 Randolph Crescent.*
> *Maida Vale.*
> *London. W.9.*
>
> Dear Mr. Hacker,
>
> Thank you for seeing me on Monday last. It is such a relief to have told you all about this whole ghastly business of the supply of British weapons to Italian terrorists. I know you will act upon this information, as you promised, and I look forward to seeing some action taken.
>
> Yours sincerely
>
> J.B. Saunders
>
> J.B. Saunders (Major)

This letter is a catastrophe. Major Saunders can prove to the world that he told me about this scandal, and that I did nothing. And it is a photocopy – he definitely has the original.

And it arrived Recorded Delivery. So I can't say I didn't get it.

I'm trapped. Unless Humphrey or Bernard can think of a way out.

September 10th
Bernard thought of a way out, thank God!

At our meeting first thing on Monday morning he suggested the Rhodesia Solution.

Humphrey was thrilled. 'Well done Bernard! You excel yourself. Of course, the Rhodesia Solution. Just the job, Minister.'

I didn't know what they were talking about at first. So Sir Humphrey reminded me of the Rhodesia oil sanctions row. 'What happened was that a member of the government had been told about the way in which British companies were sanction-busting.'

'So what did he do?' I asked anxiously.

'He told the Prime Minister,' said Bernard with a sly grin.

'And what did the Prime Minister do?' I wanted to know.

'Ah,' said Sir Humphrey. 'The Minister in question told the Prime Minister in such a way that the Prime Minister didn't hear him.'

I couldn't think what he and Bernard could possibly mean. Was I supposed to mumble at the PM in the Division Lobby, or something?

They could see my confusion.

'You write a note,' said Humphrey.

'In very faint pencil, or what? Do be practical, Humphrey.'

'It's awfully obvious Minister. You write a note that is susceptible to misinterpretation.'

I began to see. Light was faintly visible at the end of the tunnel. But what sort of note?

'I don't quite see *how*,' I said. 'It's a bit difficult, isn't it? "Dear Prime Minister, I have found that top secret British bomb detonators are getting into the hands of Italian terrorists!" How do you misinterpret that?'

'You can't,' said Humphrey, 'so don't write that. You use a more . . . circumspect style.' He chose the word carefully. 'You must avoid any mention of bombs and terrorists and all that sort of thing.'

I saw that, of course, but I didn't quite see how to write such an opaque letter. But it was no trouble to Humphrey. He delivered a draft of the letter to my red box for me tonight. Brilliant.

[*We have managed to find the letter, in the Cabinet Office files from Number Ten, subsequently released under the Thirty Year Rule. – Ed.*]

DEPARTMENT OF
ADMINISTRATIVE AFFAIRS

FROM THE MINISTER

Dear Prime Minister,   September 10th

My attention has been drawn on a personal basis to information which suggests the possibility of certain irregularities under Section 1 of the Import - Export and Custom powers (Defence) Act, 1939 (c).

Prima facie evidence suggests that there could be a case for further investigation to establish whether or not enquiries should be put in hand.

Nevertheless it should be stressed that available information is limited and the relevant facts could be difficult to establish with any degree of certainty.

Yours sincerely,

James Hacker

James Hacker

[Hacker's diary continues – Ed.]
The letter is masterly because not only does it draw attention to the matter in a way which is unlikely to be remarked, but it also suggests that *someone else* should do something about it, and ends with a sentence implying that even if they do, they won't get anywhere. So if at any future date there is an enquiry I'll be in the clear, and yet everyone will be able to understand that a busy PM might not have grasped the implications of such a letter. I signed it at once.

September 11th
I congratulated Humphrey this morning on his letter, and told him it was very unclear. He was delighted.

He had further plans all worked out. We will not send the letter for a little while. We'll arrange for it to arrive at Number Ten on the day that the PM is leaving for an overseas summit. This will mean that there will be further doubt about whether the letter was read by the PM or by the acting PM, neither of whom will remember of course.

This is the finishing touch, and will certainly ensure that the whole thing is written off as a breakdown in communications. So everyone will be in the clear, and everyone can get on with their business.

Including the red terrorists.

And I'm afraid I'm a little drunk tonight, or I wouldn't have just dictated that deeply depressing sentence.

But it's true. And I've been formulating some theories about government. Real practical theories, not the theoretical rubbish they teach in Universities.

In government you must always try to do the right thing. But whatever you do, you must never let anyone catch you trying to do it. Because doing right's wrong, right?

Government is about principle. And the principle is: don't rock the boat. Because if you do rock the boat all the little consciences fall out. And we've all got to hang together. Because if we don't we'll all be hanged separately. And I'm hanged if I'll be hanged.

Why should I be? Politics is about helping others. Even if it means helping terrorists. Well, terrorists are others, aren't they? I mean, they're not *us*, are they?

So you've got to follow your conscience. But you've also got to know where you're going. So you *can't* follow your conscience because it may not be going the same way that you are.

Aye, there's the rub.

I've just played back today's diary entry on my cassette recorder. And I realise that I am a moral vacuum too.

September 12th

Woke up feeling awful. I don't know whether it was from alcoholic or emotional causes. But certainly my head was aching and I felt tired, sick, and depressed.

But Annie was wonderful. Not only did she make me some black coffee, she said all the right things.

I was feeling that I was no different from Humphrey and all that lot in Whitehall. She wouldn't have that at all.

'He's lost his sense of right and wrong,' she said firmly. 'You've still got yours.'

'Have I?' I groaned.

'Yes. It's just that you don't use it much. You're a sort of whisky priest. You do at least know when you've done the wrong thing.'

She's right. I *am* a sort of whisky priest. I may be immoral but I'm not amoral. And a whisky priest – with that certain air of raffishness of Graham Greene, of Trevor Howard, that *je ne sais quoi* – is not such a bad thing to be.

Is it?

6
The Middle-Class Rip-off

September 24th

After my constituency surgery this morning, which I used to do every other Saturday but which I can now manage less often since I became a Minister, I went off to watch Aston Wanderers' home match.

It was a sad experience. The huge stadium was half empty. The players were a little bedraggled and disheartened, there was a general air of damp and decay about the whole outing.

I went with Councillor Brian Wilkinson, Chairman of the local authority's Arts and Leisure Committee and by trade an electrician's mate at the Sewage Farm, and Harry Sutton, the Chairman of the Wanderers, a local balding businessman who's done rather well on what he calls 'import and export'. Both party stalwarts.

Afterwards they invited me into the Boardroom for a noggin. I accepted enthusiastically, feeling the need for a little instant warmth after braving the elements in the Directors' Box for nearly two hours.

I thanked Harry for the drink and the afternoon's entertainment.

'Better enjoy it while the club's still here,' he replied darkly.

I remarked that we'd always survived so far.

'It's different this time,' said Brian Wilkinson.

I realised that the invitation was not purely social. I composed myself and waited. Sure enough, something was afoot. Harry stared at Brian and said, 'You'd better tell him.' Wilkinson threw a handful of peanuts into his mouth, mixed in some Scotch, and told me.

'I'll not mince words. We had an emergency meeting of the Finance Committee last night, Aston Wanderers is going to have to call in the receiver.'

'Bankruptcy?' I was shocked. I mean, I knew that football clubs were generally in trouble, but this really caught me unawares.

Harry nodded. 'The final whistle. We need one-and-a-half-million quid, Jim.'

'Peanuts,' said Brian.

'No thank you,' I said, and then realised that he was describing the sum of one-and-a-half-million pounds.

'Government wastes that much money every thirty seconds,' Brian added.

As a member of the government, I felt forced to defend our record. 'We do keep stringent control on expenditure.'

It seemed the wrong thing to say. They both nodded, and agreed that our financial control was so stringent that perhaps it was lack of funds for the fare which had prevented my appearance at King Edward's School prize-giving. I explained – thinking fast – that I'd had to answer Questions in the House that afternoon.

'Your secretary said you had some committee meeting.'

Maybe I did. I can't really remember that kind of trivial detail. Another bad move. Harry said, 'You know what people round here are saying? That it's a dead loss having a Cabinet Minister for an MP. Better off with a local lad who's got time for his constituency.'

The usual complaint. It's so unfair! I can't be in six places at once, nobody can. But I didn't get angry. I just laughed it off and said it was an absurd thing to say.

Brian asked why.

'There are great advantages to having your MP in the Cabinet,' I told him.

'Funny we haven't noticed them, have we, Harry?'

Harry Sutton shook his head. 'Such as?'

'Well . . .' And I sighed. They always do this to you in your constituency, they feel they have to cut you down to size, to stop you getting too big for your boots, to remind you that you need them to re-elect you.

'It reflects well on the constituency,' I explained. 'And it's good to have powerful friends. Influence in high places. A friend in need.'

Harry nodded. 'Well, listen 'ere, Friend – what we need is one-and-a-half-million quid.'

I had never imagined that they thought I could solve their financial problems. *Was* that what they thought, I wondered? So I nodded non-committally and waited.

'So will you use all that influence to help us?' asked Harry.

Clearly I had to explain the facts of life to them. But I had to do it with tact and diplomacy. And without undermining my own position.

'You see,' I began carefully, 'when I said *influence* I meant the more, er, intangible sort. The indefinable, subtle value of an input into broad policy with the constituency's interest in mind.'

Harry was confused. 'You mean no?'

I explained that anything I can do in a general sense to further the cause I would certainly do. If I could. But it's scarcely possible for me to pump one-and-a-half-million into my local football club.

Harry turned to Brian. 'He means no.'

Brian Wilkinson helped himself to another handful of peanuts. How does he stay so *thin*? He addressed me through the newest mouthful, a little indistinctly.

'There'd be a lot of votes in it. All the kids coming up to eighteen, too. You'd be the hero of the constituency. Jim Hacker, the man who saved Aston Wanderers. Safe seat for life.'

'Yes,' I agreed. 'That might just strike the press too. And the opposition. And the judge.'

They stared at me, half-disconsolately, half-distrustfully. Where, they were wondering, was all that power that I'd been so rashly talking about a few minutes earlier? Of course the truth is that, at the end of the day, I do indeed have power (of a sort) but not to really *do* anything. Though I can't expect them to understand that.

Harry seemed to think that I hadn't quite grasped the point. 'Jim,' he explained slowly, 'if the club goes to the wall it'll be a disaster. Look at our history.'

We all looked sadly around the room, which was lined with trophies, pennants, photos.

'FA Cup Winners, League Champions, one of the first teams ever into Europe,' he reminded me.

I interrupted his lecture. 'I know all this. But be fair, Harry, it's a local matter. Not ministerial.' I turned to Wilkinson. 'Brian, you're Chairman of the Borough Arts and Leisure Committee. Can't *you* do something?'

Attack is always the best form of defence. Wilkinson was instantly apologising in the same vein as me. 'You're joking. I spent half yesterday trying to raise seven hundred and eleven quid to repoint the chimney of the Corn Exchange Art Gallery.'

'That miserable place?' I asked. 'Why not just let it fall down?'

He said he'd love to. But if it did actually fall down on somebody the Council would be liable. The Borough owns the place. And, ironically, they keep getting offers for the site. There was one from Safefare Supermarkets only last month.

It was as he said this that I had one of my great flashes of inspiration. From out of nowhere 'The Idea' occurred to me. An idea of such brilliance and simplicity that I myself can, even now, be hardly sure that I thought of it all by myself, completely unprompted. But I did! It is ideas of this quality that have taken me to the top of my chosen profession and will take me still higher.

But first I had a question to ask. 'How much did Safefare offer for the site?'

Brian Wilkinson shrugged and wiped his hands on his trousers. 'About two million, I think.'

Then I hit them with it. 'So – if you sold the art gallery you could save the football club.'

They gazed at me, and then at each other, with wild surmise. Both thinking furiously.

'Can I have a look at it?' I asked.

We tore out of Aston Park. The traffic had nearly cleared, the fans dispersed, the police horses had done their Saturday afternoon cavalry charge, and all the hooligans had been trampled on or arrested. We raced through the deserted early evening streets to the Corn Exchange. It was due to shut at 5.30. We got there just after it closed.

We stepped out of Harry's Rolls in front of the art gallery, stood still, and looked up at our target. To tell the truth, I'd never really *looked* at it before. It is a Victorian monster, red-brick, stained glass, battlements and turrets, big and dark and gloomy.

'Hideous, isn't it?' I said to Brian Wilkinson.

'Yeah, well, it's a Grade II listed building, isn't it?'

That certainly is the problem.

September 25th

Today Brian, Harry and I returned to the art gallery. Fortunately it's open on Sundays too. Annie was pretty fed up this morning. I told her I was going to the art gallery but she didn't believe me. It's not really surprising – I didn't even go into any art galleries when we went to Italy a couple of years ago. My feet get so tired.

The gallery was empty when we got there. So we found the Curator, a pleasant chubby middle-aged lady, and had a little chat with her. She was awfully pleased to see us and of course I didn't tell her the purpose of our call. I just made it look like I was keeping a fatherly eye on the constituency.

I asked her how popular the gallery is. She answered that it is very popular, and smiled at me.

'You mean, a lot of people come here?'

She was careful to be honest. 'Well, I wouldn't say a lot. But it's very popular with those who come.'

A slightly evasive response. I pressed her for details; like, the daily average of visitors through the year.

'Well into double figures,' she said, as if that were rather a lot.

'How well?'

'Um – eleven, on average,' she admitted, but she added emphatically that they were all very appreciative.

We thanked her for her help and pottered off to look at the pictures. My feet started aching instantly.

At Harry's office afterwards we went over the details of the proposition. Eleven people per day at the gallery, fifteen to twenty thousand people every week at Aston Wanderers. There is no doubt in any of our minds that our plan is in the public interest.

And the plan is simplicity itself. Close the art gallery, sell it to Safefare Supermarkets, and use the money for an interest-free loan to Aston Wanderers.

Harry sounded a note of caution. 'There'd have to be a planning inquiry. Change of use. Art gallery to supermarket.'

I could see no problem. There's no question that this scheme will be immensely popular round here. There's bound to be some opposition, of course – there's opposition to *everything* – but art-lovers aren't a very powerful lobby compared to the Supporters' Club. Brian, who is also the Chairman of the Arts Committee, asked me what they could do with the paintings. I suggested that they sell them in the supermarket – if they can!

SIR BERNARD WOOLLEY RECALLS:[1]
Hacker had told me of this plan to save his local football club, but I paid no great attention to it. It seemed to me that it was a constituency matter and not relevant to his Ministerial role.

I was rather surprised to receive a telephone call from Sir Humphrey Appleby about it, asking what – precisely – our political master was up to.

Rather tactlessly I asked him how he found out about it, and was instantly reprimanded. 'Not from you, Bernard, an omission you may perhaps like to explain.'

He asked for a memo. I sent him one, describing the situation and concluding with my opinion that it would be a very popular move that the local people would support. I received a stern reply, which I have always kept. It is an excellent guideline for all policy matters connected with the Arts.

[1] In conversation with the Editors.

Cat. No. 6912

Memorandum
From The Permanent Secretary
To: B.W.   September 29th.

The Minister's scheme to demolish the Corn Exchange Art Gallery would in your opinion be popular. This is undoubtedly true. It would be distressingly popular. Hideously popular.

I ask you to take a broader view and consider the consequences.

1. <u>The Minister would be re-elected</u>

    We, of course, have no Departmental view on this matter. We do not mind whether the Minister is re-elected or not. As far as this Department is concerned, it makes very little difference who the Minister is.

2. <u>Subsidy for the Arts would be threatened</u>

    Suppose other football clubs get into difficulty. Or greyhound race tracks. Should dog racing be subsidised if football clubs are subsidised? If not, why not? You say people would want it.

    You have sadly misunderstood the purpose of subsidy. Subsidy is for Art. It is for Culture. It is not to be given to what the people want, it is for what the people don't want but ought to have. If they really want something they will pay for it themselves. The Government's duty is to subsidise education, enlightenment and spiritual uplift, not the vulgar pastimes of ordinary people. This is the thin edge of the wedge and an appalling precedent. It must be stopped.

    Please arrange a meeting between the Minister and me, asap, nominally to discuss the impending departmental reorganisation.

[Hacker's diary continues – Ed.]

September 30th

Bernard slipped an extra meeting with Sir Humphrey into my diary, first thing this morning.

My Permanent Secretary wanted to warn me personally that there is a reshuffle in the offing.

Naturally this made me a little nervous, as I wasn't sure if he was dropping an early hint about my being dropped. This was not just paranoia on my part, because I still don't know whether my deal with the Chief Whip on the matter of the bomb detonators has redounded to my credit or debit as far as the PM is concerned.

But Humphrey made it quickly clear that he was actually talking about a departmental reorganisation – what he called 'a real reshuffle'. He was warning me that we may be given extra responsibilities.

God knows if we want them! I certainly feel that I've got quite enough on my plate. But Humphrey was in no doubt that it would be a definite plus.

'We want all responsibilities, so long as they mean extra staff and bigger budgets. It is the breadth of our responsibilities that makes us important – makes *you* important, Minister. If you want to see vast buildings, huge staff and massive budgets, what do you conclude?'

'Bureaucracy,' I said.

Apparently I'd missed the point. 'No, Minister, you conclude that at the summit there must be men of great stature and dignity who hold the world in their hands and tread the earth like princes.'

I could certainly see his point, put like that.

'So that is the reason,' Humphrey continued, 'why every new responsibility must be seized and every old one guarded jealously. Entirely in your interest of course, Minister.'

A real overdose of soft-soap. In my interest perhaps, but certainly not *entirely* in my interest. He must think I was born yesterday.

I thanked him for the information and courteously dismissed him. I can really see through him nowadays.

As he was leaving he enquired about the Corn Exchange Art Gallery proposal. I was surprised he'd heard about it as it's not a matter for central government.

To my surprise he heaped abuse upon the scheme. 'It's a most imaginative idea. Very novel.'

I wondered what he'd got against it, and invited him to go on.

'Well . . .' He returned from the door to my desk, 'I just wondered if it might not be a little unwise.'

I asked him why.

'A valuable civic amenity,' he replied.

I pointed out that it is a monstrosity.

He amended his view slightly. 'A valuable civic monstrosity,' he said, and added that it contained a most important collection of British paintings.

He's obviously been misinformed. In fact, as I told him then and there, the collection is utterly unimportant. Third-rate nineteenth-century landscapes and a few modern paintings so awful that the Tate wouldn't even store them in its vaults.

'But an *important* representative collection of unimportant paintings,' insisted Sir Humphrey, 'and a great source of spiritual uplift to the passing citizenry.'

'They never go in,' I told him.

'Ah, but they are comforted to know it's there,' he said.

I couldn't see where this was leading, what it had to do with Humphrey Appleby, or how he could possibly have any views about this collection of paintings at all. He's hardly ever been north of Potters Bar.

I took a stand on a principle. I reminded him that this is a constituency matter, that it concerns the Borough Council and me as constituency MP – not as Minister – and that it was nothing at all to do with him or Whitehall.

He pursed his lips and made no reply. So I asked him *why* he was interested. To my surprise he told me that it was a matter of principle.

This astonished me. Throughout our whole fight on the question of the bomb detonators he had insisted with religious fervour that principles were no concern of his. I reminded him of this.

'Yes, Minister.' He conceded the point. 'But principle is what you've always told me that government is all about.'

I was baffled. 'What principle is at stake here?'

'The principle of taking money away from the Arts and putting it into things like football. A football club is a commercial proposition. There is no cause for subsidising it if it runs out of money.'

He seemed to think that he had just made an irrefutable statement of fact.

'Why not?' I asked.

'Why not what?'

'Why is there no cause? There's no difference between subsidising football and subsidising art except that lots more people are interested in football.'

'Subsidy,' he replied, 'is to enable our cultural heritage to be preserved.'

But for whom? For whose benefit? For the educated middle-classes. For people like Humphrey, in other words. Subsidy means they can get their opera and their concerts and their Shakespeare more cheaply than if the full cost had to be recouped from ticket sales. He thinks that the rest of the country should subsidise the pleasures of a middle-class few who want to see theatre, opera and ballet.

'Arts subsidy,' I told him simply, 'is a middle-class rip-off. The middle-classes, who run the country, award subsidies to their own pleasures.'

He was shocked. Genuinely shocked, I think. 'How can you say such a thing? Subsidy is about education and preserving the pinnacles of our civilisation. Or hadn't you noticed?' he added scathingly.

I ordered him not to patronise me. I reminded him that I also believe in education – indeed, I am a graduate of the London School of Economics.

'I'm glad to learn that even the LSE is not totally opposed to education.' he remarked. I rose above his pathetic Oxbridge joke, and remarked that there is no possible objection to subsidising sport. Sport is subsidised in many ways already. And sport is educational.

Sir Humphrey's sarcasm was in full swing. 'Education is not the whole point,' he said, having said that it *was* the whole point not two minutes earlier. 'After all, we have sex education too – should we subsidise sex perhaps?'

'Could we?' asked Bernard hopefully, waking up suddenly like the Dormouse. Humphrey scowled at him.

I was enjoying the cut and thrust of our intellectual debate, particularly as I seemed to be doing most of the cutting and thrusting.

I proposed to Humphrey that we might, in fact, choose what to subsidise by the extent of public demand. I certainly can't see anything wrong with the idea. It's democratic at least.

Humphrey normally ignores me when I'm being provocative, unless a serious policy decision of mine is at stake. But for some reason it seemed important to him to persuade me to change my mind.

'Minister,' he said, pleading for me to understand his élitist point-of-view, 'don't you see that this is the thin end of the wedge. What will happen to the Royal Opera House, on this basis? The very summit of our cultural achievement.'

As a matter of fact, I don't think that the Royal Opera House *is* the summit of our achievement. It's a very good case in point – it's all Wagner and Mozart, Verdi and Puccini. German and Italian. It's not our culture at all. Why should we subsidise the culture of the Axis Powers?

'The Royal Opera House,' I explained, 'gets about nine-and-a-half-million pounds a year of public money. For what? The public can't afford to buy thirty or forty quid seats for gala nights – and even if they could, they can't *get* them, there aren't enough. The audience consists almost entirely of big business executives, block-booked by the banks and oil companies and multi-nationals – and people like you, Humphrey. The Royal Opera House is for the Establishment at play. Why should the workers on the terraces foot the bill for the gentry in the stalls who can well afford to pay the full price for their seats?'

He stared at me as though I'd been brought in by the cat. I waited for a response. Bernard was studying his empty notepad intently.

Finally Sir Humphrey spoke. Very quietly. 'Minister, I am frankly appalled! This is savagery! Barbarism! That a Minister of the Crown should say such things – this is the end of civilisation as we know it. *And* it's a gross distortion of the truth.'

Emotive language from Humphrey! He was indeed upset. I, on the other hand, wasn't a bit upset and was thoroughly enjoying myself.

'A distortion, eh?' I replied cheerfully.

'Yes indeed. Art cannot survive without public subsidy.'

I wound him up some more. 'Did Shakespeare have public subsidy?'

'Yes of course he did.'

'No he didn't, he had patronage. That's quite different. It's a rich man spending his own money, not a committee spending other people's. Why can't the theatre live on its wits? Is it good for art to be dependent on officials and committees? Not necessarily!'

Humphrey made incoherent choking noises. I put up my hand regally, to silence him.

'And, if you persist in arguing in favour of subsidy, what about films? Films are art. Films are educational. Films are – God forbid! –

popular with the public. More than opera, anyway. So why has the Establishment ignored film subsidy?'

He tried to reply, but I refused to yield the floor. I was having much too good a time. 'I'll tell you. Simply because people like you prefer opera.'

Humphrey finally broke. He shouted me down before I'd finished speaking. This has never been known before. 'Minister, films are *commercial*!' He said this with all the contempt of a man who lives in a very high publicly-funded ivory tower.

Then he stood up. Clearly he was not prepared for me to bring the meeting to a close, as is the normal protocol. He had had enough, and was leaving.

'If you will excuse me, Minister, I have to leave early tonight. I simply cannot continue with this appalling discussion.' And he walked swiftly to the door.

I asked him where he was going in such a hurry.

He instantly slowed down and, his eyes moving shiftily from side to side, replied that he was going nowhere in particular.

I didn't like his walking out on me, and I told him that I insisted we talk the matter through. Apart from the immense pleasure of winding him up, I wanted to establish that my constituency affairs were nothing to do with him. Also, I was instinctively suspicious.

'I can't talk about this any further,' he said, flapping a bit and looking at his watch. 'I have to dress . . . I mean . . .'

He faltered and looked at me like a guilty hamster.

What a wonderful coincidence. I smiled lazily. 'Dress?' I asked as casually as I could. 'Where are you going?'

He drew himself up and squared his shoulders.

'Since you insist on knowing – I'm going to the Royal Opera House.'

'Gala performance, is it?'

'Yes it is, since you ask.'

'Lots of Permanent Secretaries going to be there?'

'Some, no doubt.'

I waved him away. 'Off you go, then,' I said graciously. 'I don't want to make you late for your works' outing.'

He stared at me through narrow little eyes, filled with pure hatred. I smiled back at him.

'Well, that's what it is, isn't it? What's on tonight, by the way?'

'*The Flying Dutchman.*'

'Ah. Another of our European partners.'

He turned his head and swept out. I've never enjoyed a meeting so much in my whole life. Bernard, I think, had never enjoyed one less.

[*At the Opera that evening Sir Humphrey Appleby had a drink in the Crush Bar with Sir Ian Whitworth, Permanent Secretary of the Department of the Environment. We have found an account of the meeting in Appleby's private diary – Ed.*]

Had a chat with Ian W. over a couple of large G and T's and those delicious little smoked salmon sandwiches in the Crush Bar.

He's having problems with one of his Ministers. Not the Secretary of State, who is easily handled, but one of the junior Ministers: Giles Freeman, the Parly Sec.

Discussed the impending planning inquiry into the sale and re-development of the Corn Exchange Art Gallery site. Warned him that it was rather important that we get the right result.

Ian reminded me that his planning inspectors are absolutely independent and there can be no question of undue influence. Quite right too.

On the other hand, if it were a question of his giving certain informal guidelines, putting the inquiry in the right perspective and explaining the background to facilitate an informed appreciation of the issues and implications, he agreed that such a course would be regarded as entirely proper.

Then he asked me what it was exactly that I wanted him to fix. I explained that it was a question of a proposed local authority demolition of a Grade II listed building. He misunderstood my intentions at first. He said that he would be only too happy to arrange it, there would be no problems: they'd been knocking down listed buildings all over the place.

I explained that the proposal had to be *rejected*. This amazed him, naturally. And he demanded an explanation. I was forced to reveal that if the sale goes through the proceeds will be used to save the local football club from bankruptcy.

He was visibly shaken. We were unable to continue this conversation as the interval bell went at that moment. Never send to know for whom the bell tolls – it tolls for the Arts Council.

[*Appleby Papers JAL/REL 14041*]

[*The following day Sir Humphrey Appleby received an urgent letter, delivered by hand, from Sir Ian Whitworth, see opposite – Ed.*]

**DEPARTMENT OF
THE ENVIRONMENT**

From the Permanent Secretary

1st October

Dear Humphrey,

I cannot think where that appalling idea came from. If you allow the principle of money being taken from the Arts and given to ordinary people to enjoy themselves, where will it end?

Your Lord and Master may be getting rather het up over the sweaty masses, but I beg you to do your utmost to put an end to this nonsense somehow.

There is no knowing to what this might lead. Today a Midlands art gallery goes to support a local football club — tomorrow the Royal Opera House grant goes to modernise Wembley Stadium.

For my part, I shall certainly keep a special eye on the planning inquiry. As you know, I cannot influence the Inspector, but it should prove helpful if I appoint a chap who is due for promotion.

And I'll see that he's briefed properly, so that the guidelines make it quite clear that the real issue is civilisation versus barbarism.

Yours ever,

Ian.

[A reply from Sir Humphrey Appleby – Ed.]

**MINISTRY OF
ADMINISTRATIVE AFFAIRS**

From the Permanent Under Secretary of State

2/x

Dear Ian,

As you know, I'm completely in agreement with your view of this shocking affair. Glad to hear that you're taking what steps you can.

Clearly we cannot have Arts money going to support popular sports. It's just subsidising self-indulgence.

See you at Traviata next week, if not before?

Yours

Humphrey

[Hacker's diary continues – Ed.]
October 3rd
My usual diary session with Bernard was full of interest this morning. Though I was in a hurry today he insisted on a brief talk with me before we did anything else.

'There is something I should like to suggest to you, Minister, if I may be so bold.'

I told him to be as bold as he liked.

He told me that, in his opinion, I shouldn't get involved with the art gallery/football club affair. I told him he was being rather bold.

'Better for me to be bold than for you to be stumped, Minister.' I like Bernard. He's wasted in Whitehall.

He then informed me that it is axiomatic in Whitehall (though news to me, I must say) that an MP should never get involved in a planning inquiry in his own constituency.

Apparently this is because the local issues are usually finely balanced. Therefore you're bound to offend as many constituents as you please. Either way, you can't win. The same problem as the integrated national transport policy, in fact. And Bernard emphasised that it becomes especially dangerous to become involved if there's a powerful quango lurking in the wings.

This sounded all very sensible in theory, and I was grateful for Bernard's support and care. But in this case I'm not sure that the local arguments *are* finely balanced. I told Bernard that everyone will be on the same side except for a few wet long-haired scruffy art lovers.

Bernard took this on board, and made no direct reply. He simply suggested that we now went through my diary for the morning. I thought he'd conceded my point until we examined the diary closely.

10.15 a.m. The Secretary General of the Arts Council
(The biggest quango of them all)
10.45 a.m. The Historic Monuments Association
11.00 a.m. The National Trust
11.15 a.m. The County Landowners Association
11.30 a.m. The Council for the Preservation of Rural England
11.45 a.m. The Country Crafts and Folklore Council
I gazed at Bernard, non-plussed.

'Rural England?' I asked, picking one of the appointments out at random.

'Yes,' said Bernard and made a vague gesture towards the window. 'There's quite a lot of it out there.'

'But why are all these people coming to see me?'

'The Corn Exchange,' he explained patiently. 'It's the Arts and Architecture mafia.'

'So who are the Country Crafts and Folklore Council?'

'The raffia mafia.' He wasn't joking it seems. 'All very influential people. They've all come out of the woodwork. There'll be letters in *The Times*, hostile articles in the Sundays, you'll be accused of vandalism. And you can be sure they'll orchestrate plenty of opposition in your constituency.'

I had a nasty feeling now that he could be right. But I am determined to fight on. This is one I can win.

I admonished Bernard. 'I didn't ask you to put any of these people in my diary, Bernard. What were you thinking of?'

'I was thinking of Sir Humphrey, Minister. He asked me to.'

I told Bernard that I intended to support my excellent scheme, come what may.

The rest of the day was spent in interminable meetings of excruciating boredom listening to all the pressure groups. Tonight I'm feeling absolutely exhausted.

October 4th

Bernard displayed even more ingenuity and tenacity today.

Having taken on board that my art gallery demolition plan is irrevocable, he produced a document for my inspection when I arrived at the office this morning.

He was actually asking me to approve it. He described it as the Local Government Allowances Amendment No. 2 to this year's regulations. 'What is it?' I asked.

He had written me a briefing, summarising the purpose of the document. It's a Statutory Instrument to be laid before the House. 'As Minister responsible for local government we need you to authorise that the revised Paragraph 5 of No 2 Regulations 1971 shall come into operation on the 18th of March next, revoking Regulation 7 of the Local Government Allowances Amendment Regulations 1954 (b).'

I asked him what he meant, as I took the briefing and gazed at it.

So he showed me the explanatory note, which adds that 'These regulations are to make provision for prescribing the amounts of attendance and financial loss allowances payable to members of local authorities.'

I didn't pay much attention to Bernard's summary, because I was mesmerised by the document itself. I've kept a copy.

Explanatory Note:
Regulation 3 of the Local Government Allowances Amendment Regulations 1971 ("the 1971 Regulations") substituted a new regulation for Regulation 3 of the 1954 Regulations. Regulation 3 of the Local Government Allowances Amendment Regulation 1972 ("the 1972 Regulations") further amends Regulation 3 of the 1954 Regulations by increasing the maximum rates of attendance and financial loss allowance.

Regulation 7 of 1982 Regulations revoked both Regulations 3 and 5 of the 1971 Regulations, Regulation 5 being a regulation revoking earlier spent regulations with effect from 1st. April next.

These regulations preserve Regulations 3 and 5 of the 1971 Regulations by revoking Regulation 7 of the 1972 Regulations.

[*Hacker's diary continues – Ed.*]
Isn't it remarkable that this immortal prose should be described as an 'explanatory note'?

I finished reading it and looked at Bernard.

'I think that's quite clear, isn't it?' he said.

'Do I have to bother with all this piddling gobbledegook?' I replied.

He was slightly put out. 'Oh, I'm sorry, Minister. I thought that this would be an opportune moment for you to ensure that, as a result of your Ministerial efforts, local councillors would be getting more money for attending council meetings.'

I suddenly realised what he was driving at. I glanced back at Bernard's summary. There it was, in black and white *and* plain English: 'Amounts of attendance and financial loss allowances payable to members of local authorities.' So *that's* what it all means!

He had done excellently. This is indeed an opportune moment to display some open-handed generosity towards members of local authorities.

He asked if he could make one further suggestion. 'Minister, I happen to know that Sir Humphrey and Sir Ian Whitworth have been having discussions on this matter.'

'Ian Whitworth?'

Bernard nodded. 'The Corn Exchange is a listed building. So it's one of his planning inspectors who will be conducting the inquiry. Sir Humphrey and Sir Ian will be laying down some "informal" guidelines for him.'

I was suspicious. Informal guidelines? What did this mean?

Bernard explained carefully. 'Guidelines are perfectly proper. Everyone has guidelines for their work.'

It didn't sound perfectly proper to me. 'I thought planning inspectors were impartial,' I said.

Bernard chuckled. 'Oh *really* Minister! So they are! Railway trains are impartial too. But if you lay down the lines for them, that's the way they go.'

'But that's not *fair!*' I cried, regressing forty years.

'It's politics, Minister.'

'But Humphrey's not supposed to be in politics, he's supposed to be a civil servant. I'm supposed to be the one in politics.'

Then the whole import of what I'd blurted out came home to me. Bernard was nodding wisely. Clearly he was ready and willing to explain what political moves I had to make. I asked him how Humphrey and Ian would be applying pressure to the planning inspector.

'Planning inspectors have their own independent hierarchy. The only way they are vulnerable is to find one who is anxious for promotion.'

'Can a Minister interfere?'

'Ministers are our Lords and Masters.'

So that was the answer. Giles Freeman, the Parly Sec at the Department of the Environment, is an old friend of mine. I resolved to explain the situation to Giles and get him to intervene. He could, for instance, arrange to give us a planning inspector who doesn't care about promotion because he's nearing retirement. Such a man might even give his verdict in the interests of the community.

All I said to Bernard was: 'Get me Giles Freeman on the phone.'

And to my astonishment he replied: 'His Private Secretary says he could meet you in the lobby after the vote this evening.'

I must say I was really impressed. I asked Bernard if he ever thought of going into politics. He shook his head.

'Why not?'

'Well, Minister, I once looked up politics in the *Thesaurus*.'

'What does it say?'

'"Manipulation, intrigue, wire-pulling, evasion, rabble-rousing, graft . . ." I don't think I have the necessary qualities.'

I told him not to underestimate himself.

[*Four days later Sir Humphrey Appleby received another letter from Sir Ian Whitworth – Ed.*]

**DEPARTMENT OF
THE ENVIRONMENT**

From the Permanent Secretary

5th October

Dear Humphrey,

More bad news. It seems that your Minister has got at Giles Freeman, our ghastly Party Sec. He has personally insisted on a different planning inspector to the one I chose. One who would be sympathetic to Hacker's scheme.

This is rather worrying, to say the least. There is now every danger that the planning inspector might make up his own mind.

It seems that there is likely to be a great deal of local support for this scheme.

Any ideas?

Ian.

149

[*We can find no written reply to this cry for help. But two days later Sir Humphrey and Sir Ian had lunch with Sir Arnold Robinson, the Cabinet Secretary. This account appears in Sir Humphrey's private diary, and was apparently written in a mood of great triumph – Ed.*]

At lunch with Arnold and Ian today I brought off a great coup.

Ian wanted to discuss our planning problem. I had invited Arnold because I knew that he held the key to it.

Having briefed him on the story so far, I changed the subject to discuss the Departmental reorganisation which is due next week. I suggested that Arnold makes Hacker the Cabinet Minister responsible for the Arts.

Arnold objected to that on the grounds that Hacker is a complete philistine. I was surprised at Arnold, missing the point like that. After all, the Industry Secretary is the idlest man in town, the Education Secretary's illiterate and the Employment Secretary is unemployable.

The point is that Hacker, if he were made Minister responsible for the Arts, could hardly start out in his new job by closing an art gallery.

As for Ian, he was either puzzled or jealous, I'm not sure which. He objected that the reorganisation was not meant to be a Cabinet reshuffle. I explained that I was not suggesting a reshuffle: simply to move Arts and Tele-communications into the purview of the DAA.

There is only one problem or inconsistency in this plan: namely, putting arts and television together. They have nothing to do with each other. They are complete opposites, really.

But Arnold, like Ian, was more concerned with all the power and influence that would be vested in me. He asked me bluntly if we wouldn't be creating a monster department, reminding me that I also have Administrative Affairs and Local Government.

I replied that Art and local government go rather well together – the art of jiggery-pokery. They smiled at my aphorism and, as neither of them could see any other immediate way of calling Hacker to heel, Arnold agreed to implement my plan.

'Bit of an artist yourself, aren't you?' he said, raising his glass in my direction.

[*Appleby Papers NG/NDB/FX GOP*]

October 10th

Good news and bad news today. Good on balance. But there were a few little crises to be resolved.

I was due to have a meeting with my local committee about the Aston Wanderers/Art Gallery situation.

But Humphrey arrived unexpectedly and demanded an urgent word with me. I told him firmly that my mind was made up. Well, it *was* – at that stage!

'Even so, Minister, you might be interested in a new development. The government reshuffle.'

This was the first I'd heard of a reshuffle. A couple of weeks ago he'd said it would be just a reorganisation.

'Not *just* a reorganisation, Minister. A *reorganisation*. And I'm delighted to say it has brought you new honour and importance. In addition to your existing responsibilities, you are also to be the Cabinet Minister responsible for the Arts.'

This was good news indeed. I was surprised that he'd been told before I had been, but it seems he was with the Cabinet Secretary shortly after the decision was taken.

I thanked him for the news, suggested a little drinkie later to celebrate, and then told him that I was about to start a meeting.

'Quite so,' he said. 'I hope you have considered the implications of your new responsibilities on the project you are discussing.'

I couldn't at first see what rescuing a football club had to do with my new responsibilities. And then the penny dropped! How on earth would it look if the first action of the Minister for the Arts was to knock down an art gallery?

I told Bernard to apologise to the Councillors, and to say that I was delayed or something. I needed time to think!

So Humphrey and I discussed the art gallery. I told him that I'd been giving it some thought, that it was quite a decent little gallery, an interesting building, Grade II listed, and that clearly it was now my role to fight for it.

He nodded sympathetically, and agreed that I was in a bit of a fix. Bernard ushered in the Councillors – Brian Wilkinson leading the delegation, plus a couple of others – Cllrs. Noble and Greensmith.

I had no idea, quite honestly, what I was going to say to them. I ordered Humphrey to stay with me, to help.

'This is my Permanent Secretary,' I said.

Brian Wilkinson indicated Bernard. 'You mean he's only a temp?' Bernard didn't look at all pleased. I couldn't tell if Brian was sending him up or not.

I was about to start the meeting with a few cautious opening remarks when Brian plunged in. He told me, with great enthusiasm, that it was all going great. All the political parties are with the plan. The County Council too. It was now unstoppable. All he needed was my Department's approval for using the proceeds from the sale of the art gallery as a loan to the club.

I hesitated. 'Yes,' I said. 'Well – um . . . there is a snag.'

Wilkinson was surprised. 'You said there weren't any.'

'Well, there is.' I couldn't elaborate on this terse comment

151

because I just couldn't think of anything else to say.

'What is it?' he asked.

My mind was blank. I was absolutely stuck. I said things like 'apparently . . . it seems . . . it has emerged,' and then I passed the buck, 'I think Sir Humphrey can explain it better,' I said desperately.

All eyes turned to Sir Humphrey.

'Um . . . well. It just can't be done, you see,' he said. It looked for a dreadful moment that he was going to leave it at that – but then, thank God, inspiration struck. 'It's because the art gallery is a trust. Terms of the original bequest. Or something,' he finished lamely.

I picked up the ball and carried on running with it. Blindly. 'That's it,' I agreed emphatically, 'a trust. We'll just have to find something else to knock down. A school. A church. A hospital. Bound to be something.'

Councillor Brian Wilkinson's jaw had dropped. 'Are we supposed to tell people that you've gone back on your word? It was your idea to start with.'

'It's the law,' I whined, 'not me.'

'Well, why didn't you find this out till now?'

I had no answer. I didn't know what to say. I broke out in a cold sweat. I could see that this could cost me my seat at the next election. And then dear Bernard came to the rescue.

He was surreptitiously pointing at a file on my desk. I glanced at it – and realised that it was the gobbledegook amending Regulation 7 of the Amendment of Regulations Act regulating the Regulation of the Amendments Act, 1066 and all that.

But what was it all about? Cash for Councillors? *Of course!*

My confidence surged back. I smiled at Brian Wilkinson and said, 'Let me be absolutely frank with you. The truth of the matter is, I *might* be able to get our scheme through. But it would take a lot of time.'

Wilkinson interrupted me impatiently. 'Okay, take the time. We've spent enough.'

'Yes,' I replied smoothly, 'but then something else would have to go by the board. And the other thing that's taking my time at the moment is forcing through this increase in Councillors' expenses and allowances. I can't put my personal weight behind both schemes.'

I waited. There was silence. So I continued. 'I mean, I suppose I could forget the increased allowances for Councillors and concentrate on the legal obstacles of the art gallery sale.'

There was another silence. This time I waited till one of the others broke it.

Finally Wilkinson spoke. 'Tricky things – legal obstacles,' he remarked. I saw at once that he understood my problem.

So did Humphrey. 'This is a particularly tricky one,' he added eagerly.

'And at the end of the day you might still fail?' asked Wilkinson.

'Every possibility,' I replied sadly.

Wilkinson glanced quickly at his fellow Councillors. None of them were in disagreement. I had hit them where they lived – in the wallet.

'Well, if that's the way it is, okay,' Wilkinson was agreeing to leave the art gallery standing. But he was still looking for other ways to implement our scheme because he added cheerfully, 'There's a chance we may want to close Edge Hill Road Primary School at the end of the year. That site could fetch a couple of million, give or take.'

The meeting was over. The crisis was over. We all told each other there were no ill-feelings, and Brian and his colleagues agreed that they would make it clear locally that we couldn't overcome the legal objections.

As he left, Brian Wilkinson told me to carry on the good work.

Humphrey was full of praise. 'A work of art, Minister. Now, Minister, you have to see the PM at Number Ten to be officially informed of your new responsibilities. And if you'll excuse me, I have to go and dress.'

'Another works' outing?'

'Indeed,' he said, without any air of apology.

I realised that, as Minister responsible for the Arts, the Royal Opera House now came within my purview. And I've hardly ever been.

'Um . . . can I come too?' I asked tentatively.

'Yes Minister,' he replied with great warmth.

And we had a jolly good evening – good music, great singing, smart people and some delicious little smoked salmon sandwiches in the Crush Bar.

Maybe I was wrong. The middle-classes are entitled to a few perks, aren't they?

7

The Skeleton in the Cupboard

November 4th

An interesting situation emerged today from another meeting to which my old friend Dr Cartwright came.

It was a fairly dull routine meeting to start with, all about local government administration. As Humphrey predicted, our Department was increasing in size, staffing and budget. He is plainly in his element. So far, however, it hasn't involved much in the way of policy decisions, which is where I come in.

We'd reached item seven on the agenda, and so far it had been pretty uneventful. The only interest had been in Bernard's pedantic linguistic quibbles, about which he is becoming obsessional.

'Item seven,' I asked, 'what's it about?'

'If I may just recapitulate,' began Sir Humphrey.

Bernard made a little sign and caught my eye.

'Yes Bernard?'

'Um – one can't actually recapitulate an item if one hasn't started it yet,' he volunteered.

Sir Humphrey, who doesn't like to be corrected by *anyone,* let alone a mere Private Secretary, thanked him coldly and proceeded to complete his sentence, thus demonstrating to Bernard that the correction was both impertinent and unnecessary.

'Thank you Bernard, where would we be without you? Minister, may I just, recapitulating *on our last meeting* and on our submissions which you have doubtless received in your boxes . . .'

I was thoroughly amused, and not paying full attention. 'Doubtless,' I interrupted cheerfully, and then realised that I didn't know what he was talking about. After all, they give me mountains of paper to read virtually every day, I can't remember everything.

'Which minutes?' I asked.

'On the proposal to take disciplinary action against the South West Derbyshire County Council.'

I still had no idea what the proposal was. But I didn't like to admit it, it's always better to make them think that one is completely on top of the job. So I casually asked Bernard to remind me.

The problem was that the council in question had failed to complete their statutory returns and supply us with the statistical information that the DAA requires.

I asked what we were going to do about it. Apparently a policy decision was required from me. Sir Humphrey offered me assorted alternatives. 'A rebuke from the Minister, a press statement about their incompetence, withholding various grants and allowances, or, ultimately, as you are no doubt fully aware . . .'

'Yes, yes,' I interrupted helpfully.

'Good,' he said, and fell silent.

Again I was in a bit of a hole. I had no idea what he'd been about to say. But clearly he was waiting for my comments.

'I'm fully aware of . . . what?' I prompted him.

'What?'

'What am I fully aware of?'

'I can't think of anything.' Then he realised what he'd said because he added hastily, 'I mean, I can't think what you are . . .'

'You were saying,' I explained, feeling somewhat embarrassed by now. (After all, seven assorted officials of various ages and ranks were silently watching my display of confusion and ineptitude.) 'You were saying: "ultimately, as I'm fully aware" . . .'

'Ah yes, Minister'. Now he was on the ball again. 'Ultimately, taking the local authority to court.'

I asked if a failure to complete returns is all that serious.

Eight officials looked shocked! I was told categorically that it is not merely serious, but catastrophic!

I wanted to know why. Sir Humphrey was quick to explain.

'If local authorities don't send us the statistics we ask for, then government figures will be nonsense. They'll be incomplete.'

I pointed out that government figures are a nonsense anyway. No one denied it, but Bernard suggested that Sir Humphrey wanted to ensure that they are a complete nonsense.

He was rewarded with another withering look from his boss.

I was worried about making an example of South West Derbyshire, which I happened to know is controlled by my party. Humphrey realised that this was on my mind, and raised the matter with me. I responded by suggesting that we pick on an opposition council instead.

This went down badly. I can't see why. What does he expect? Anyway, the suggestion was met with pursed lips from Sir Humphrey, and everyone else looked down at their blotters.

So I asked if South West Derbyshire are really all that bad. And suddenly everyone had plenty to say.

One Under-Sec told me that they won't return their blue forms (whatever they are, something to do with finance I think). An Assistant-Sec told me that they replied to the DAA's Ethnic Personnel Breakdown Request in longhand, on the back of a departmental circular. And a delightfully attractive lady Assistant-Sec was appalled because she still hadn't received their Social Worker Revised Case-load Analysis for the last two quarters. Or their Distributed Data Processing Appropriation Tables. 'They're unbelievable,' she said. 'Really evil.'

This was a definition of evil? Someone who doesn't return his blue form? 'Yes,' I said with heavy irony, 'I don't see how life still goes on in South Derbyshire.'

Sir Humphrey took my remark at face value. 'Exactly, Minister. They really are in a class of their own for incompetence.'

Still worried about my party problems, I enquired if they had no redeeming features. And my old friend Dr Cartwright piped up cheerfully. 'Well, it is interesting that . . .'

Sir Humphrey cut right across him. 'So if that's all right, Minister, we can take appropriate coercive action?'

Dr Cartwright had another try. 'Except that the Minister might . . .'

Again Sir Humphrey interrupted him. 'So can we take it you approve?' It was all beginning to look distinctly fishy.

I decided not to give an immediate answer. 'It's a difficult one. They're friends of ours.'

'They're no friends of good administration.'

I refused to be pressured. 'Give me twenty-four hours. I'll have to square the party organisation. Get the Chairman invited to a drink-ies do at Number Ten or something. Soften the blow.'

And I insisted that we press on to the next item.

As the meeting broke up I noticed Dr Cartwright hovering, as if he wanted a private word with me. But Sir Humphrey took him by the arm and gently guided him away. 'I need your advice, Dick, if you could spare me a moment.' And they were gone.

Having thought about this overnight, I think I'll question Bernard more closely tomorrow.

November 5th

A fascinating day.

I raised the matter with Bernard as soon as I got to the office. I told him that my instincts told me that there is a good reason not to discipline South West Derbyshire.

'Furthermore, Dr Cartwright seemed to be trying to tell me something. I think I'll drop in on him.'

'Oh, I wouldn't do that Minister,' he said it rather too hastily.

'Why not?'

He hesitated. 'Well, it is, er, understood that if Ministers need to know anything it will be brought to their attention. If they go out looking for information, they might, er they might . . .'

'Find it?'

'Yes.' He looked sheepish.

I remarked that it may be 'understood', but it's not understood by me.

Bernard obviously felt he had better explain further. 'Sir Humphrey does not take kindly to the idea of Ministers just dropping in on people. "Going Walkabout", he calls it.'

I couldn't see anything wrong with that. I reminded him that the Queen does it.

He disagreed. 'I don't think she drops in on Under-Secretaries. Not in Sir Humphrey's department.'

I took a firm line. I asked Bernard for Dr Cartwright's room number.

He virtually stood to attention. 'I must formally advise you against this, Minister,' he said.

'Advice noted,' I said. 'What's his room number?'

'Room 4017. Down one flight, second corridor on the left.'

I told him that if I wasn't back within forty-eight hours he could send a search party.

SIR BERNARD WOOLLEY RECALLS[1]

I well recall the day that Hacker went walkabout. This was the kind of situation that highlighted the dilemma of a Minister's Private Secretary. On the one hand I was expected to be loyal to the Minister, and any sign of disloyalty to him would mean that I had blotted my copybook. On the other hand, Sir Humphrey was my Permanent Secretary, my career was to be in the Civil Service for the next thirty years, and I owed a loyalty there also.

This is why high fliers are usually given a spell as Private Secretary. If

[1] In conversation with the Editors.

157

one can walk the tightrope with skill and manage to judge what is proper when there is a conflict, then one may go straight to the top, as I did.

[*'Walking the tightrope' is Sir Bernard's phrase for betraying confidences from each side to the other while remaining undetected. – Ed.*]

After the Minister left his office I telephoned Graham Jones, Sir Humphrey Appleby's Private Secretary. I let him know that the Minister had gone walkabout. I had no choice but to do this, as I had received specific instructions from Sir Humphrey that this should be discouraged. [*i.e. prevented. – Ed.*]

I actually counted out ten seconds on my watch, from the moment I replaced the receiver, so well did I know the distance from his office to the Minister's, and Sir Humphrey entered the office on the count of 'ten'.

He asked me what had happened. Carefully playing it down, I told him that the Minister had left his own office. Nothing more.

Sir Humphrey seemed most upset that Hacker was, to use his words, 'loose in the building'. He asked me why I had not stopped him.

As it was my duty to defend my Minister, even against the boss of my own department, I informed Sir Humphrey that (a) I had advised against it, but (b) he was the Minister, and there was no statutory prohibition on Ministers talking to their staff.

He asked me to whom the Minister was talking. I evaded the question, as was my duty – clearly the Minister did not want Sir Humphrey to know. 'Perhaps he was just restless' is what I think I said.

I recall Sir Humphrey's irritable reply: 'If he's restless he can feed the ducks in St James's Park'.

Again he asked who the Minister was talking to, and again I evaded – under more pressure by this time – by seeking confirmation that the Minister could talk to anyone he liked.

Sir Humphrey's reply made it clear to me that he attached the greatest departmental importance to the issue. 'I am in the middle of writing your annual report,' he told me. 'It is not a responsibility that either of us would wish me to discharge while I am in a bad temper.' Then he asked me *again* to whom the Minister was talking.

I realised that I had gone as far as I safely could in defending the Minister's interests. And yet as his Private Secretary, I had to be seen to be standing up for him.

So I resorted to a well-tried formula. I asked for Sir Humphrey's help. Then I said: 'I can quite see that you should be told if the Minister calls on an outsider. But I can't see that it is necessary to inform you if he just wanted, to take a purely hypothetical example, to check a point with, say, Dr Cartwright. . . .'

He interrupted me, thanked me, and left the room. I called '4017' after him – well, why not?

I had passed the test with flying colours. I had managed to see that Sir Humphrey knew what he wanted, without actually telling him myself.

The hypothetical example was, and is, an excellent way of dealing with such problems.

[*Hacker's diary continues – Ed.*]

When I got to Cartwright's office I certainly learned a thing or two. Cartwright was delighted to see me, and told me quite openly that I had been misled at yesterday's meeting. I was intrigued.

'But all those things they told me about South West Derbyshire – aren't they true?'

'They may be, for all I know.'

I asked him precisely what he was saying. To my surprise I got a completely straight answer. I can see why he's going to rise no higher.

'I'm saying that, nevertheless, South West Derbyshire is the most efficient local authority in the UK.' And he blinked at me pleasantly from behind his half-moon reading glasses.

I was surprised, to say the least. 'The most efficient – But I'm supposed to be ticking them off for being the *least* efficient.'

Then he showed the figures.

This in itself was a surprise, as I'd been told that they didn't send us the figures. This was true – but no one had told me that they kept their own records perfectly well, which were available for us to see.

And the figures are impressive. They have the lowest truancy record in the Midlands, the lowest administrative costs per council house, the lowest ratio in Britain of council workers to rate income, and a clean bill of public health with the lowest number of environmental health officers.[1]

And that's not all. It seems that virtually all the children can read and write, despite their teachers' efforts to give them a progressive education. 'And,' Cartwright finished up, 'they have the smallest establishment of social workers in the UK.'

From the way he reported this fact I gathered he thought that this was a good thing. I enquired further.

'Oh yes. Very good. Sign of efficiency. Parkinson's Law of Social Work, you see. It's well known that social problems increase to occupy the total number of social workers available to deal with them.'

It was at this critical juncture that Sir Humphrey burst into Cartwright's office. I believe that his arrival in Cartwright's office at that moment was no coincidence.

We had a pretty stilted conversation.

'Oh, Minister! Good Heavens!'

---

[1] Ratcatchers.

'Oh. Hello Humphrey!'

'Hello Minister.'

'What a coincidence.'

'Yes. Indeed. What a surprise.'

'Yes.'

'Yes.'

For some reason he was making me feel guilty, and I found myself trying to explain my presence there.

'I was just, er, passing.'

'Passing?'

'Yes. Passing.'

'Passing. I see.' He considered my explanation for a moment. 'Where were you going?'

I was trapped. I had no idea what else was on Cartwright's floor. I decided to be vague.

'Oh,' I said airily, 'I was just going . . . past.' I said it as if 'past' were a specific place to go. 'Past the door,' I added. I was aware that I sounded fearfully unconvincing but I blundered on. 'Cartwright's – Richard's door. Dick's door. So I thought "hello"!'

'And then did you think anything further?' He is relentless.

'Yes. I thought, why should I just pass the door? I might as well . . . open it.'

'Good thinking, Minister. That's what doors are for.'

'Quite.' I summoned up my courage and finally got to the point. 'And I'd remembered one or two points I wanted to clear up.'

'Good. What points?'

I couldn't see why I should tell him. Or why I shouldn't be in Cartwright's office. Or why he was successfully making me feel guilty? Or why he should consider that he had the right to approve everything that the DAA staff say to me. He behaves as though they are his staff, not mine. [*They were. – Ed.*]

But I also couldn't see how not to answer him.

'Oh, just some odd points,' I replied finally, making a suitably vague gesture.

He waited. Silence. Then he repeated it. 'Just some odd points.'

'Yes,' I said.

'How odd?' he asked.

'Well it's not all *that* odd,' I said, argumentatively, wilfully misunderstanding him. 'We had a meeting yesterday, didn't we?'

Sir Humphrey was now tired of the fencing.

'Minister, may I have a word with you?'

'Certainly,' I said, 'as soon as Richard and I have . . .'

He interrupted. 'I mean now.'

Now it was my turn to embarrass him a little. 'Okay. Go ahead.' I knew he wouldn't want to talk in front of one of his juniors.

'Upstairs, Minister, in your office if you please.'

'But I'm sure Richard doesn't mind.'

'Upstairs Minister. I'm sure Dr Cartwright can spare you for a few moments.'

Cartwright missed the heavy sarcasm completely. 'Oh yes,' he said with an obliging smile.

Sir Humphrey opened the door. Having been made to feel like a naughty schoolboy, I marched out of Cartwright's office.

I wonder how he knew I was in that office. I know Bernard wouldn't have told him, so somebody must have seen me and reported it. I might as well be in the Soviet Union. Somehow I've got to get my freedom – but that involves winning the psychological war against Humphrey. And somehow, he always manages to make me feel guilty and unsure of myself.

If only I could find a chink in his armour. If I ever do, he's *had* it!

Anyway, that tense little sparring match in Cartwright's office wasn't the end of the matter. A few minutes later, back in my office after an icy silent journey up in the lift and along the endless corridors, the row came to a head.

He told me that I cannot just go around talking to people in the Department, and expressed the sincere hope that such a thing would not occur again.

I could scarcely believe my ears. I ordered him to explain himself.

'Minister, how can I advise you properly if I don't know who's saying what to whom? I must know what's going on. You simply cannot have completely private meetings. And what if you're told things that aren't true?'

'If they're not true you can put me right.'

'But they may be true.'

'In *that* case . . .' I began triumphantly. He interrupted me, correcting himself hastily.

'That is, not *entirely* false. But misleading. Open to misinterpretation.'

I faced him with a straight question. 'The fact is, you're just trying to keep things from me, aren't you Humphrey?'

He was indignant. 'Absolutely not Minister. Records must be kept. You won't be here forever, nor will we. In years to come it may be vital to know what you were told. If Cartwright were moved tomorrow, how could we check on your information?'

On the face of it, that was a specious argument. 'Cartwright *isn't* being moved tomorrow,' I said.

'Oh, isn't he?' came the insolent response.

Bernard interrupted us. Alex Andrews of *The Mail* wants to do an interview with me tomorrow. I agreed of course. I told Bernard to stay with us and minute our conversation. Humphrey had given me *his* views on my private meeting with Cartwright. Now he was going to hear *mine*.

I began by repeating what Cartwright had told me: namely, that in his opinion – and the opinion of everyone who knows anything about local government – the South West Derbyshire County Council is the most efficient in the country.

'Inefficient, I think he means, Minister.'

'Efficient, Humphrey. Effective. Economical. They're just not particularly interested in sending pieces of blue paper to Whitehall.'

Humphrey then explained something that I hadn't quite grasped yet. Apparently they *have* to return those sodding blue forms, it's a statutory requirement.

And we know why. We know who decreed that it should be so.

Even so, statutory requirements can be overlooked occasionally. Discretion can be exercised. So I asked Humphrey what happens if they don't send in their blue forms. South West Derbyshire carries on, rather well apparently.

'But,' said Humphrey, not seeing at all what I was getting at, 'if they don't send us the information and plans and requests for permission, well, what are we here for?'

An excellent question, as I told him immediately. I asked it at once. 'What *are* we here for?'

'To collate the information, inspect the plans, and grant or withhold permission.'

'And if we didn't?' I asked.

He gazed at me studiously. I might have been talking Ancient Chinese, for all the sense I was making to him.

'I'm sorry, Minister, I don't understand.'

I persevered. 'If we didn't. If we weren't here and we didn't do it – then what?'

'I'm sorry Minister, you've lost me.'

Yet again, Humphrey demonstrates that his trouble is that he is concerned with means and not ends.

[*Many civil servants of the time deflected criticisms about ends and means by stating flippantly that the only ends in administration are loose ends. If administration is viewed in a vacuum this is, of course, true. Adminstration can have no end in itself, and is eternal.*

Perhaps it is because there are no ends that people talk about moving in government circles. – Ed.]

[*Hacker's Diary continues. – Ed.*]
The upshot of the whole argument was that I refused to discipline the most efficient local authority in Britain, on the grounds that I would look like an idiot if I did.

Sir Humphrey told me that was my job. I *think* he meant to discipline South West Derbyshire, rather than to look like an idiot, but I'm not certain. He said that I had no alternative to consider, no discretion to exercise, and that the Treasury and the Cabinet Office insist.

[*By Cabinet Office Sir Humphrey clearly meant the Cabinet Secretary rather than the PM. But he could never have said so – the fiction had to be preserved that Britain was governed by Ministers who told civil servants what to do, not vice versa. – Ed.*]
I still refused to co-operate.

'Minister. You don't seem to understand. It's not up to you or me. It's the law.'

And there we left it. I felt a bit like a dog refusing to go for a walk – sitting down and digging in my paws while being dragged along the pavement on my bottom.

But there must be some way out. The more I think of it, the less willing I am to discipline that council until there is *really* no alternative.

And the more I think of it, the more I conclude that Bernard must have told Humphrey that I'd gone to talk to Cartwright.

November 6th
I had no free time to talk to Bernard on his own yesterday.

But first thing this morning, while I was doing my letters, I had a serious word with Bernard. I asked him how Humphrey had found out yesterday that I was with Cartwright.

'God moves in a mysterious way,' he said earnestly.

'Let me make one thing quite clear,' I said, 'Sir Humphrey is not God. Okay?'

Bernard nodded. 'Will you tell him, or shall I?' he replied.

Very droll. But again I asked him how Humphrey knew where to find me.

I am fortunate that my dictaphone had been left running. I noticed it some minutes later. As a result I am able to record his reply for posterity in this diary.

'Confidentially, Minister, everything you tell me is in complete confidence. So, equally, and I'm sure you appreciate this, and by appreciate I don't actually mean appreciate, I mean understand, that everything that Sir Humphrey tells me is in complete confidence. As indeed everything I tell you is in complete confidence. And for that matter, everything I tell Sir Humphrey is in complete confidence.'

'So?' I said.

'So, in complete confidence, I am confident you will understand that for me to keep Sir Humphrey's confidence and your confidence means that my conversations must be completely confidential. As confidential as conversations are between you and me are confidential, and I'll just get Alex Andrews as he's been waiting to see you Minister.'

There it is. Word for word. What was I supposed to make of that? Nothing, of course.

My meeting with Alex Andrews of *The Mail* was today. I'd been very keen to fit him in at the earliest opportunity. I'd been hoping for a Profile, or something of that sort, but no such luck. Still, I've done him a good turn today, it's no skin off my nose, and perhaps he'll do the same for me one day.

He asked for my help in a fascinating story that he had just come across. 'Did you know that your government is about to give away forty million pounds' worth of buildings, harbour installations, a landing strip to a private developer? For nothing?'

I thought he was having me on. 'Forty million pounds?'

'Scout's Honour.'

'Why ask me?' I said. Suddenly I had a dreadful moment of panic. 'I didn't do it, did I?'

[*You may think that Hacker should have known if he had done it. But a great many things are done in a Minister's name, of which he may have little or no awareness. – Ed.*]

Alex smiled, and told me to relax. Thank God!

Then he told me the story. It goes back a long way. Almost thirty years ago the Ministry of Defence took a lease on a Scottish island. They put up barracks, married quarters, an HQ block, and the harbour and airstrip. Now the lease has expired and they all become the property of the original landowner. And he is turning it into an instant holiday camp. Chalets, yachting marina, staff quarters – it's all there. He is going to make a fortune.

I listened, open-mouthed. 'But he can't do that!' I began. 'The law says that . . .'

Andrews interrupted me. 'You're talking about English law. This contract was under Scottish law and some idiot didn't realise the difference.'

I was relieved that at least I am in the clear. Even *The Mail* can't blame me for a cock-up in the early fifties. Though I'm sure they would if they could. And I couldn't at first see what he wanted from me. He already had the story. Thirty years late, as quick with the news as ever – still, not bad for Fleet Street!

They are running the story tomorrow. But apparently they don't want to leave it at that. The Editor wants Alex to follow up with an investigative feature. He wants him to go through the files, and find out exactly how it happened.

I couldn't see the point, not now.

'Well,' he explained, 'there may be lessons for today. And we might find who was responsible.'

I asked why it would matter? It would, in any case, have been handled by quite a junior official.

He nodded. 'Okay, but that was thirty years ago. He could be in a very senior position now, even a Permanent Secretary, running a great department, responsible for spending billions of pounds of public money.'

A very unlikely eventuality, in my opinion. These hacks will do anything to try and find a story where there isn't one.

He agreed it was pretty unlikely. But he asked to see the papers.

Naturally I had to be a bit cautious about that. I can't just hand files over, as he well knows. But I advised him that, as it was a thirty year lease that was in question, he would be able to get the papers from the Public Record Office under the Thirty Year Rule.

He was unimpressed. 'I thought you'd say that. I've asked for them already. But I want a guarantee that I *will* get them. All of them.'

I hate being asked to guarantee anything. I don't really think it's fair. And anyway, was I in a position to? 'Well,' I said, carefully feeling my way, 'Defence papers are sometimes . . .'

He interrupted me. 'Don't come that one. It's not top security.

Look, you made a manifesto commitment about telling voters the facts. This is a test case. Will you guarantee that no papers are removed before the files are opened?'

I could see no reason not to give him that guarantee. 'Fine,' I said, throwing caution to the winds. 'No problem.'

'Is that a promise?' Journalists are suspicious bastards.

'Sure,' I said with a big reassuring smile.

'A real promise? Not a manifesto promise?'

Some of these young Fleet Street fellows can be really rather insulting.

'Your trouble, Alex,' I said 'is that you can't take yes for an answer.'

'Because otherwise,' he continued as if I hadn't even spoken, 'we do the feature on Ministers ratting on manifestos.

Clearly I shall now have to stand by that promise. It's fortunate that I have every intention of doing so.

[*The following day* The Mail *ran the story, exactly as predicted in Hacker's diary, see opposite. That night Sir Humphrey's diary contains the following entry. – Ed.*]

Horrible shock.

A story in today's *Mail* about the Glenloch Island base.

I read it on the 8.32 from Haslemere to Waterloo. Was seized instantly by what Dr Hindley calls a panic attack. A sort of tight feeling in the chest, I felt I couldn't breathe, and I had to get up and walk up and down the compartment which struck one or two of the regulars on the 8.32 as a bit strange. Or perhaps I just *think* that because of the panic attack.

Fortunately Valium did the trick as the day wore on, and I'll take a few Mogadon tonight.[1]

I tell myself that no one will ever connect that incident with me, and that it's all ancient history anyway, and that that's the last that anyone will want to know about it.

I tell myself that – but somehow it's not helping!

Why has this come up now, so many years later, when I thought it was all forgotten?

If only there was someone I could talk to about this.

Oh my God . . .

[*Hacker's diary continues – Ed.*]

November 7th

They ran that story in *The Mail* today. Quite amusing.

---

[1] Brand of sleeping pills in common use in the 1980s.

Developer's Multi-Million Pound Bonanza From Government Error

By ALEX ANDREWS

An elementary mistake by a junior government official thirty years ago has cost British tax payers at least forty million pounds. The lucky beneficiary is a German property developer.

November 8th

Today was the happiest day of my ministerial life.

All my prayers were answered.

As Humphrey and I were finishing up our weekly departmental meeting I asked him if he'd seen the story in yesterday's *Mail*.

'I'm not sure,' he said.

I reminded him. I knew he must have seen it, someone must have drawn his attention to it. 'You know,' I added, 'about that frightful cock-up thirty years ago over the terms of that Scottish island base.'

Now, as I think back, he seemed to flinch a little as I said 'that frightful cock-up'. Though I must say, I wasn't really aware of it at the time.

Anyway, he did remember the article, and he said that he believed that he *had* glanced at it, yes.

'I must say,' I said, chuckling, 'I think it's pretty funny – forty million quid down the tube. Someone really boobed there, didn't they?'

He nodded and smiled, a little wanly.

'Still, it couldn't happen in your Department could it?'

'No,' he said with absolute firmness. 'Oh no. Absolutely.'

I said that I'd been wondering who it was.

'That, Minister, is something that we shall never know.'

I pointed out that it must be on the files. Everything is always put in writing, as he so constantly reminds me.

Humphrey agreed that it would be on the record somewhere, but it would take ages to find out and it's obviously not worth anyone's time.

'Actually, you're wrong there,' I said. '*The Mail* are doing a big feature on it when the papers are released under the thirty year rule. I've promised them a free run of all the files.'

Humphrey literally rocked backwards on his feet.

'Minister!'

I was slightly shaken by his anger. Or was it anger? I couldn't tell.

'It's all right, isn't it?' I asked anxiously.

Yes, it *was* anger! 'All right? *All right*? No, it is certainly not all right.'

I asked why not. He told me it was 'impossible and unthinkable.' That didn't sound like much of an explanation to me, and I said as much.

'It . . . it's . . . top security, Minister.'

'A few barracks?'

'But there were secret naval installations, anti-submarine systems, low level radar towers.'

I pointed out that he couldn't possibly know what had been there. He agreed at once, but added – rather lamely, I thought – that that's the sort of thing those island bases always had.

'They'll have been dismantled,' I said. His objection was clearly quite irrelevant.

'But the papers will have references.'

'It's ancient history.'

'Anyway,' he said with evident relief, 'we'd have to consult. Get clearances.'

A few months ago I would have accepted that sort of remark from Humphrey. Now, I'm just a little older and wiser.

'Who from?' I asked.

He looked wildly about, and spoke completely incoherently. 'Security implications . . . MI5, MI6 . . . the national interest . . . foreign powers . . . consult our allies . . . top brass . . . CIA . . . NATO, SEATO, Moscow!'

'Humphrey,' I asked carefully, 'are you all right?'

'*Not* Moscow, no, I don't mean Moscow,' he corrected himself hastily. I got the impression that he was just saying the first words that came into his head, and that the word Moscow had been uttered simply because it rhymed.

He could see I wasn't convinced, and added: 'There could be information that would damage people still alive.'

This seemed to matter to him greatly. But it cut no ice with me.

'Whoever drafted that contract,' I insisted, '*ought* to be damaged if he's still alive.'

'Oh, quite, absolutely, no question of protecting officials. Of course not. But responsible Ministers . . .'

I interrupted him. I wasn't the least concerned about some Minister who'd been responsible thirty years ago. It couldn't matter less. Anyway, the other lot were in office then, so it's fairly amusing.

I simply couldn't figure out the reason for his intense opposition to releasing these papers. I asked him why he was *so* concerned.

He sat back in his chair and crossed his legs casually. 'I'm not. Not at all. I mean, not personally. But it's the principle, the precedent . . . the . . . the . . .' he was lost for words '. . . the policy.'

Trapped. I'd got him. 'Policy's up to me Humphrey, remember?' I said with a smile. And before he could continue the argument I added, 'And I've promised, so it's done now, okay?'

He just sat there, sagging slightly, looking at me. Evidently he was trying to decide whether or not to say something. Finally he gave up. He stood wearily and, without looking at me, walked silently out of the room and shut the door behind him.

He seemed tired, listless, and quite without his usual energy.

Bernard had been present throughout the meeting. He waited, patiently, as usual, to be either used or dismissed.

I gazed at the door which Humphrey had closed quietly behind him.

'What's the matter with Humphrey?' I asked. There was no reply from Bernard. 'Have I done something wrong?' Again there was no reply. 'There *aren't* any security aspects, are there?' This time I waited a while, but answer came there none. 'So what is the problem?' I turned to look at Bernard, who appeared to be staring vacantly into space like a contented heifer chewing the cud.

'Am I talking to myself?'

He turned his gaze in my direction.

'No Minister, I am listening.'

'Then why don't you reply?'

'I'm sorry,' he said. 'I thought your questions were purely rhetorical. I can see no reason for Sir Humphrey to be so anxious.'

And then the penny dropped.

Suddenly I saw it.

I didn't know how I could have been so blind. So dumb. And yet, the answer – obvious though it was – seemed scarcely credible.

'Unless . . .' I began, and then looked at Bernard. 'Are you thinking what I'm thinking?'

He looked puzzled. 'I don't think so Minister,' he replied cautiously, and then added with a flash of cheerful honesty, 'I'm not thinking anything really.'

'I *think*,' I said, uncertain how to broach it, 'that I smell a rat.'

'Oh. Shall I fetch an Environmental Health Officer?'

I didn't like actually to put my suspicions into words. Not yet. I thought I'd go carefully. So I asked Bernard how long Sir Humphrey had been here at the Department of Administrative Affairs.

'Oh, all his career, hasn't he? Ever since it was founded.'

'When was that?' I asked.

'1964. Same time that they started the Department of Economic Affairs . . .' he stopped dead, and stared at me, wide-eyed. 'Oh,' he said. 'Now I think I'm thinking what you're thinking.'

'Well?' I asked.

He wanted to be cautious too. 'You're thinking: where was he before 1964?'

I nodded slowly.

'It'll be in *Who's Who.*' He stood, then hurried to the glass-fronted mahogany bookcase near the marble fireplace. He fished out *Who's Who*, talking as he leafed through the pages. 'He must have been in some other Department, and been trawled when the DAA started. ['*Trawled*', *i.e. caught in a net, is the standard Civil Service word for 'head-hunting' through other departments. – Ed.*]

He ran his forefinger down a page, and said in one sentence: 'Ah here we are oh my God!'

I waited.

Bernard turned to me. 'From 1950 to 1956 he was an Assistant Principal at the Scottish Office. Not only that. He was on secondment from the War Office. His job was Regional Contracts Officer. Thirty years ago.'

There could be no doubt who the culprit was. The official who had chucked away that forty million pounds of the taxpayers' money was the current Permanent Under-Secretary of the Department of Administrative Affairs, Sir Humphrey Appleby, KCB, MVO, MA (Oxon).

Bernard said, 'This is awful,' but his eyes were twinkling.

'Terrible,' I agreed, and found myself equally unable to prevent a smile creeping across my face. 'And the papers are all due for release in a few weeks' time.'

I suddenly felt awfully happy. And I told Bernard to get Humphrey back into my office at once.

He picked up the phone and dialled. 'Hello Graham, it's Bernard. The Minister wondered if Sir Humphrey could spare some time for a meeting some time in the next couple of days.'

'At once,' I said.

'In fact, some time during the course of today is really what the Minister has in mind.'

'At once,' I repeated.

'Or to be precise, any time within the next sixty seconds really.'

He listened for a moment, then replaced the receiver. 'He's coming round now.'

'Why?' I was feeling malicious. 'Did he faint?'

We looked at each other in silence. And we both tried very hard not to laugh.

Bernard's mouth was twitching from the strain.

'This is very serious Bernard.'

'Yes Minister,' he squeaked.

I was, by now, crying from the effort not to laugh. I covered my eyes and my face with my handkerchief.

'No laughing matter,' I said, in a strangled muffled gasp, and the tears rolled down my cheeks.

'Absolutely not,' he wheezed.

We recovered as best we could, shaking silently, but didn't dare look at each other for a little while. I sat back in my chair and gazed reflectively at the ceiling.

'The point is,' I said, 'how do I best handle this?'

'Well, in my opinion . . .'

'The question was purely rhetorical Bernard.'

Then the door opened, and a desperately worried little face peeped around it.

It was Sir Humphrey Appleby. But not the Humphrey Appleby I knew. This was not a God bestriding the Department of Administrative Affairs like a colossus, this was a guilty ferret with shifty beady eyes.

'You wanted a word Minister?' he said, still half-hidden behind the door.

I greeted him jovially. I invited him in, asked him to sit down and – rather regretfully – dismissed Bernard. Bernard made a hurried and undignified exit, his handkerchief to his mouth, and curious choking noises emanating from it.

Humphrey sat in front of me. I told him that I'd been thinking about this Scottish island scandal, which I found very worrying.

He made some dismissive remark, but I persisted. 'You see, it probably hasn't occurred to you but that official could still be in the Civil Service.'

'Most unlikely,' said Sir Humphrey, presumably in the hope that this would discourage me from trying to find out.

'Why? He could have been in his mid-twenties then. He'd be in his mid-fifties now,' I was enjoying myself thoroughly. 'Might even be a Permanent Secretary.'

He didn't know how to reply to that. 'I, er, I hardly think so,' he said, damning himself further.

I agreed, and said that I sincerely hoped that anyone who made a howler like that could *never* go on to be a Permanent Secretary. He nodded, but the expression on his face looked as though his teeth were being pulled out without an anaesthetic.

'But it was so long ago,' he said. 'We can't find out that sort of thing now.'

And then I went for the jugular. This was the moment I'd been waiting for. Little did I dream, after he had humiliated me in front of Richard Cartwright, that I would be able to return the compliment so soon.

And with the special pleasure of using his own arguments on him.

'Of course we can find out,' I said. 'You were telling me that everything is minuted and full records are always kept in the Civil Service. And you were quite right. Well, legal documents concerning a current lease could not possibly have been thrown away.'

He stood. Panic was overcoming him. He made an emotional plea, the first time I can remember him doing such a thing. 'Minister, aren't we making too much of this? Possibly blighting a brilliant career because of a tiny slip thirty years ago. It's not such a lot of money wasted.'

I was incredulous. 'Forty million?'

'Well,' he argued passionately, 'that's not such a lot compared with Blue Streak, the TSR2, Trident, Concorde, high-rise council flats, British Steel, British Rail, British Leyland, Upper Clyde Ship Builders, the atomic power station programme, comprehensive schools, or the University of Essex.'

[*In those terms, his argument was of course perfectly reasonable. – Ed.*]

'I take your point,' I replied calmly. 'But it's still over a hundred times more than the official in question can have earned in his entire career.'

And then I had this wonderful idea. And I added: 'I want you to look into it and find out who it was, okay?'

Checkmate. He realised that there was no way out. Heavily, he sat down again, paused, and then told me that there was something that he thought I ought to know.

Surreptitiously I reached into my desk drawer and turned on my little pocket dictaphone. I wanted his confession to be minuted. Why not? All conversations have to be minuted. Records must be kept, mustn't they?

This is what he said. 'The identity of this official whose alleged responsibility for this hypothetical oversight has been the subject of recent speculation is not shrouded in quite such impenetrable obscurity as certain previous disclosures may have led you to assume, and, in fact, not to put too fine a point on it, the individual in question was, it may surprise you to learn, the one to whom your present interlocutor is in the habit of identifying by means of the perpendicular pronoun.'

'I beg your pardon?' I said.

There was an anguished pause.

'It was I,' he said.

I assumed a facial expression of deep shock. 'Humphrey! No!'

He looked as though he was about to burst into tears. His fists clenched, knuckles whitened. Then he burst out. 'I was under pressure! We were overworked! There was a panic! Parliamentary questions tabled.' He looked up at me for support. 'Obviously I'm not a trained lawyer, or I wouldn't have been in charge of the legal unit.'

[*True enough. This was the era of the generalist, in which it would have seemed sensible and proper to put a classicist in charge of a legal unit or a historian in charge of statistics. – Ed.*] 'Anyway – it just happened. But it was thirty years ago, Minister. Everyone makes mistakes.'

I was not cruel enough to make him suffer any longer. 'Very well Humphrey,' I said in my most papal voice. 'I forgive you.'

He was almost embarrassingly grateful and thanked me profusely.

I expressed surprise that he hadn't told me. 'We don't have any secrets from each other do we?' I asked him.

He didn't seem to realise that I had my tongue in my cheek. Nor did he give me an honest answer.

'That's for you to say, Minister.'

'Not entirely,' I replied.

Nonetheless, he was clearly in a state of humble gratitude and genuinely ready to creep. And now that he was so thoroughly softened up, I decided that this was the moment to offer my *quid pro quo*.

'So what do I do about this?' I asked. 'I've promised to let *The Mail* see all the papers. If I go back on my word I'll be roasted.' I looked him straight in the eye. 'On the other hand, I might be able to do something if I didn't have this other problem on my plate.'

He knew only too well what I was saying. He's done this to me often enough.

So, immediately alert, he asked me what the other problem was.

'Being roasted by the press for disciplining the most efficient council in Britain.'

He saw the point at once, and adjusted his position with commendable speed.

After only a momentary hesitation he told me that he'd been thinking about South West Derbyshire, that obviously we can't change the law as such, but that it might be possible to show a little leniency.

We agreed that a private word to the Chief Executive would suffice for the moment, giving them a chance to mend their ways.

I agreed that this would be the right way to handle the council. But it still left one outstanding problem: how would I explain the missing papers to *The Mail*?

We left it there. Humphrey assured me that he would give the question his most urgent and immediate attention.

I'm sure he will. I look forward to seeing what he comes up with tomorrow.

November 9th
When I arrived at the office this morning Bernard informed me that Sir Humphrey wished to see me right away.

He hurried in clutching a thin file, and looking distinctly more cheerful.

I asked him what the answer was to be.

'Minister,' he said, 'I've been on to the Lord Chancellor's Office, and this is what we normally say in circumstances like this.'

He handed me the file. Inside was a sheet of paper which read as follows:
'This file contains the complete set of available papers except for:
  (a) a small number of secret documents.
  (b) a few documents which are part of still active files.
  (c) some correspondence lost in the floods of 1967.
  (d) some records which went astray in the move to London.
  (e) other records which went astray when the War Office was incorporated into the Ministry of Defence.
  (f) the normal withdrawal of papers whose publication could give grounds for an action of libel or breach of confidence or cause embarrassment to friendly governments.'
[*1967 was, in one sense, a very bad winter. From the Civil Service point of view it was a very good one. All sorts of embarrassing records were lost. – Ed.*]

I read this excellent list. Then I looked in the file. There were no papers there at all! Completely empty.

'Is *this* how many are left? None?'

'Yes Minister.'

**DEPARTMENT OF
ADMINISTRATIVE AFFAIRS**

This file contains the complete set of available

papers except for:

(a) a small number of secret documents

(b) a few documents which are part of
     still active files.

(c) some correspondence lost in the floods
     of 1967

(d) some records which went astray in the
     move to London

(e) other records which went astray when the
     War Office was incorporated into the
     Ministry of Defence.

(f) the normal withdrawal of papers whose
     publication could give grounds for an
     action on libel or breach of confidence
     or cause embarrassment to friendly governments.

Approved J.H.